THE OXFORD LIBRARY OF FRENCH CLASSICS
General Editor: Robert Baldick

PROSPER MÉRIMÉE

THE VENUS OF ILLE
and other stories

PROSPER MÉRIMÉE

The Venus of Ille
and other stories

Translated by
JEAN KIMBER

Introduced by
A. W. RAITT

London
OXFORD UNIVERSITY PRESS
NEW YORK   TORONTO
1966

Oxford University Press, Ely House, London W.1

GLASGOW NEW YORK TORONTO MELBOURNE WELLINGTON
CAPE TOWN SALISBURY IBADAN NAIROBI LUSAKA ADDIS ABABA
BOMBAY CALCUTTA MADRAS KARACHI LAHORE DACCA
KUALA LUMPUR HONG KONG

This translation is based on *Romans et Nouvelles*
published by Gallimard in the Bibliothèque de la Pléiade, 1962

Printed in Great Britain
by Richard Clay (The Chaucer Press), Ltd.,
Bungay, Suffolk

8912

Contents

CONTENTS

Introduction

IN an article on his friend the explorer Victor Jacquemont, Mérimée once wrote: 'I have never known anyone with a heart more truly sensitive than Jacquemont. His was a loving and tender nature, but he took as much care to hide his emotions as others do to disguise evil inclinations. In our youth, we were shocked by the spurious sentiment of Rousseau and his imitators. There came about a reaction which, as usually happens, went too far in the opposite direction. We wanted to be strong, and we made fun of sentimentality. Perhaps Victor was involuntarily giving way to this tendency of our generation.' In Mérimée's analysis of the psychology of his contemporaries, this fear of being thought soft and the desire to protect one's inmost feelings from bruising contacts with an unsympathetic world are factors so constant that they betray his own carefully guarded secret. The detachment, the cynicism, the harshness which characterize his style of narration are defence mechanisms designed to preserve him from excessive involvement with the sufferings of the characters whom he observes with such apparent indifference.

It is this paradoxical coupling of a preoccupation with strong emotion and instinctive reluctance to be visibly moved which gives Mérimée his special excellence as a short-story writer. At a time when his Romantic contemporaries were yielding all too easily to a demonstrative and lachrymose prolixity, Mérimée deliberately opted for a reserved, almost offhand style, for effects which were baldly stated or obliquely implied, but never exaggerated, for feelings which were always subjected to the scrutiny of a corrective irony. But at the same time, he was drawn to subjects of near-melodramatic intensity—the slaughter of a son by his father, the tragic fate of a cargo of Negro slaves, the senseless death of a lover at the height of his happiness, the eerie murder of a bridegroom by a statue. By using a simple, laconic style to recount events highly charged with passion, Mérimée produced tales of overpowering impact and created the prototypes of what we now recognize as the modern short story.

Mérimée's remarkable narrative efficiency has often led to the reproach of coldness. It has been said, time and again, that he possesses no qualities except impeccable technical dexterity. André Gide spoke for many readers of Mérimée when, on reading *The Storming of the Redoubt*, he noted 'an unbearable impression of homework well done and of useless perfection'. It is certain that Mérimée never attempts anything beyond his capabilities and that he is always in complete control of his medium. Words are used with telling economy, description is unobtrusively integrated into the action, character is revealed by an admirable choice of gesture and dialogue, and the mechanism of each story functions with unerring precision. A tale like *Mateo Falcone* is a masterpiece not so much of understatement as of exact statement: every detail counts, from the introductory account of the *maquis* to Mateo's final order to send for his new heir. Even in a longer work like *The Venus of Ille* where he appears to adopt the discursive, conversational manner of an uninvolved observer, he uses none but the most essential notations. Not many writers have equalled him in packing an explosive content into a few deceptively casual lines.

But to infer from this that Mérimée stands aloof from normal human reactions is to ignore the undercurrents which swirl dangerously beneath the calm surface of his tales. In the opening pages of *The Etruscan Vase*, there is a curiously revealing sketch of Auguste Saint-Clair, in which Mérimée's friends had no difficulty in recognizing the author himself. 'He was naturally tender-hearted and affectionate, but, at an age when lasting impressions are acquired too easily, his demonstrative nature had drawn upon him the sarcasm of his comrades. He was proud and ambitious, and set store by the opinion of others, as children do. Henceforth he made a point of hiding any outward sign of what he considered a discreditable weakness. He attained his end, but his victory cost him dear. He learnt to hide the emotions of his tender heart from others, but repressing them only increased their force a hundredfold. In Society he won the sorry reputation of being heartless and indifferent; and, when alone, his anxious imagination plagued him with torments all the more hideous in that he could not reveal them to anyone.' Such moments of involuntary confession are very rare with the reticent Mérimée, who normally took every precaution to keep the prying gaze of the public away from his own emotions, and their rarity makes them all the more significant.

There are two ways in which the true depths of his sensibility are indicated by his tales: by his recurrent pre-occupation with the brutality of primitive passions, and by his aggressive scepticism about the real nature of the seemingly more refined intercourse of civilized society. In the early stories especially, Mérimée appears fascinated by outbursts of often murderous instincts in simple, uneducated people—a Corsican peasant, an African savage, or, somewhat later, a Spanish gipsy. The same obsession with uninhibited, bloodthirsty lusts and hates is carried over into the learned works which Mérimée devoted to the most fevered and lawless periods of Roman, Spanish, Russian, and French history. Like Stendhal, he seems to have regarded the free expression of fierce passions as the natural prerogative of man, which had been repressed and stultified, and like Stendhal, he derived considerable pleasure from occasions when the mask of hypocrisy dropped to reveal the naked face of bestiality.

The corollary to this predilection for primitive violence is a strong reluctance to accept at its face value the coinage of polite social behaviour. Mérimée delights in demonstrating how vile, how selfish, how stupid his fellow men can be, for all their supposedly elevated motives and gracious manners.

In *The Game of Backgammon*, Roger, a proud and courageous officer, commits a despicable crime, that of cheating at cards, not so much because he needs the money as out of sheer greed: 'When I cheated that Dutchman, my only thought was to win twenty-five napoleons, that was all . . . I, to hold my honour in less esteem than twenty-five napoleons! . . . What baseness!' In *The Etruscan Vase*, Mérimée mercilessly exposes the idiocy to which a man in love can sink; Saint-Clair's jealousy is awakened by a chance word, appeased by a rose in his mistress's hair, aroused again by the sight of an Etruscan vase, and finally dissipated by the breaking of the vase. But in the meantime, he has insulted a friend in a fit of childish pique and dies in the ensuing duel. The tone of *The Abbé Aubain* is much lighter; there, a high-born lady, tempted by the scandal of making a young priest fall in love with her, is outwitted by the priest, whose only interest is in preferment. Perhaps Mérimée's most remarkable essays in psychological penetration are *The Double Misunderstanding* and *Arsène Guillot*, unfortunately too long to be included in the present selection. In both of them, Mérimée devastatingly analyses the fallibility and uncertainty of human motives, in the one case those of a virtuous married woman who in a matter of hours succumbs to the blandishments of a callous philanderer whom she does not even love, in the other those of a charitable lady who befriends a lovelorn *grisette*, only to end by stealing her lover.

There is more in these tales than the sardonic misanthropy which apparently inspires them. Mérimée resolutely refuses to sentimentalize over Saint-Clair, yet one feels an unspoken compassion with the man whose reticence towards the woman he loved needlessly provoked his own death. In *Arsène Guillot*, though he is as lucid in unmasking that unconscious egoism which masquerades as charity as André Gide was to be in *The Pastoral Symphony*, there is real sympathy in the contrasting portrait of the simple, spontaneous, and honest *grisette*. Even *The Double Misunderstanding*, superficially one of his most cynical works, ends on a note of

sudden pathos, when he remarks that the two main characters might perhaps have found happiness in mutual love, if
either had understood the other. These fleeting glimpses of
tenderness reveal that Mérimée was not wholly the hardened
sceptic that he would have us believe, but rather a man so
bruised by disappointment that he could never afford to take
any feeling too seriously lest it hurt him unbearably.

Admittedly, Mérimée's all-embracing scepticism came in
the end to poison the sources of his art. Already in one or
two of the early tales there are disconcerting moments when
the author coolly negates the very effects he has been seeking
to create. When in *The Game of Backgammon* the captain's
story is interrupted by the sighting of a whale, one senses
Mérimée turning his back on the tragic events he has been
relating. In *The Venus of Ille,* if the narrator seems as much
concerned about archaeological discoveries as about the fate
of his host's son, it is because Mérimée, too, is becoming
increasingly mistrustful of even the most basic human
emotions. The culmination of these doubts about the value
of feeling and of fiction came in 1847, with the appearance
of a revised version of *Carmen*, first published in 1845. The
story had originally ended with Don José's dramatic account
of the murder of Carmen. But Mérimée saw fit to append to
it a pedantic disquisition on the language of the gipsies,
concluding with dry irony: 'That is quite enough to give the
readers of *Carmen* a flattering idea of my knowledge of the
Romany tongue.' One can only see this painfully contrived
anti-climax as a conscious rejection of the artistic illusion so
convincingly built up in the body of the work. It is as if
Mérimée, afraid that people might think he took his own
inventions too seriously, was anxious to demonstrate that
he felt nothing but disdain for them.

This unhappy tendency to denigrate his own creations
ended by sapping Mérimée's confidence in creative literature.
After 1846, he turned to history, to archaeology, to critic-
ism, and to translation, abandoning his former joy in story-
telling and providing ample justification for Charles Du Bos'

dictum: 'Scepticism may well be the beginning of wisdom, but it is the end of art.' It was only shortly before his death, and in response to pressure to provide entertainment for the ladies of Napoleon III's court, that Mérimée returned briefly to imaginative writing. This belated attempt to recapture the inspiration of earlier years was far from an unqualified success. Mérimée had lost much of his inventive verve and almost all of his ability to believe in the creatures of his own imagination, with the result that, of the three tales which he wrote in the 1860s, only *Lokis* struck him as worthy of publication. The other two, published posthumously, both offer evidence of the erosion of his talent. *Djoumane* suffers from being constructed around the facile device—already used in *Il Viccolo di Madama Lucrezia*—of evoking a mystery which turns out not to be one at all. *The Blue Chamber* follows the same pattern, with comic intent, but is little more than a coarse joke tricked out in elegant French.

Lokis is a more complex and ambitious work, and it raises the question of Mérimée's attitude to the fantastic. From the outset of his career, he had been curious about the strange and the supernatural, and they had provided him with some of his most striking successes, notably *The Venus of Ille*. But his interest was purely external and never involved the slightest inclination to believe in anything beyond the world of the senses. One of the most perceptive of his recent critics, M. P.-G. Castex, reminds us that Mérimée once wrote to Mme de la Rochejaquelein: 'I like imagining ghosts and fairies. I could make my hair stand on end by telling myself ghost stories. But, despite the entirely physical impression which I feel, that doesn't prevent me from not believing in ghosts, and on that score my incredulity is so great that, if I saw a spectre, I still wouldn't believe in it.' So tales like *The Vision of Charles XI* and *The Venus of Ille* are masterly exercises in the art of conquering the reader's disbelief, rather than manifestations of belief on Mérimée's part. However, by the time he wrote *Lokis*, he had lost the faculty of persuading himself that the fantastic was even theoretically possible, and though he labours to recreate the sinister atmosphere of *The Venus of Ille* (rather too visibly, since he repeats the tricks of the earlier tale—the donnish narrator, the marriage preparations, the presages of disaster, and the slaying on the wedding night), he fails because he makes the story turn, not on the intervention of a supernatural though credible force but on a scabrous physiological impossibility. Mérimée's last tales clothe his sexual obsessions in a specious narrative disguise; they lack any vestige of the inner life of the masterpieces of his youth.

If the obvious limitations of Mérimée's art prevent him from equalling the incomparable originality of his great friend Stendhal, the lasting popularity of his tales testifies not only to their faultless workmanship but also to the hidden presence in them of an intriguing, contradictory but eminently human personality. Mérimée's pervasive scepticism may have deprived him of the true greatness to which his acute intelligence and his technical brilliance might otherwise have led, but so long as clear-sightedness and contained emotion are valued, he will continue to be read with profit and enjoyment.

A. W. RAITT

The Venus of Ille

I was going down the last slope of the Canigou, and, although the sun had already set, I could distinguish on the plain the houses of the little town of Ille, towards which I was making.

'You know, no doubt,' I said to the Catalan who had been my guide since the previous day, 'where Monsieur de Peyrehorade lives?'

'Do I know where?' he exclaimed. 'I know his house as well as I know my own; and if it wasn't so dark I would point it out to you. It is the prettiest in Ille. Monsieur de Peyrehorade is a rich man; and he is marrying his son to a lady even richer than himself.'

'Is the marriage to take place soon?' I asked.

'Very soon; indeed, the fiddlers may already have been ordered for the wedding. Perhaps it will be tonight, or tomorrow, or the day after, for all I know. It'll be at Puygarrig; for the son is to marry Mademoiselle de Puygarrig. Oh, it'll be a very grand affair!'

I had been recommended to call on Monsieur de Peyrehorade by my friend Monsieur de P., who told me he was a very learned antiquarian and extremely good-natured. He would be delighted to show me all the ruins for miles around. So I had been looking forward to visiting with him the district surrounding Ille, which I knew to be rich in monuments both of ancient times and the Middle Ages. This wedding, of which I now heard for the first time, would upset all my plans. I said to myself that I was going to be a killjoy; but I was expected, and as Monsieur de P. had written to say I was coming, I should have to present myself.

'I'll bet you, Monsieur,' said my guide, when we were

already in the plain—'I'll bet you a cigar that I can guess why you're going to Monsieur de Peyrehorade's.'

'But that is not a difficult thing to guess', I replied, offering him a cigar. 'At this hour, after travelling six leagues on the Canigou hills, the main thing is to have supper.'

'Yes, but tomorrow? . . . I'll bet that you have come to Ille to see the idol. I guessed that when I saw you drawing pictures of the Saints at Serrabona.'

'The idol! What idol?' The word had aroused my curiosity.

'What! Did nobody tell you at Perpignan that Monsieur de Peyrehorade had found an idol in the earth?'

'Do you mean a statue in terracotta, in clay?'

'No, I don't. It's made of copper, and there's enough of it to make hundreds of coins. It weighs as much as a church bell. It was a good way down, at the foot of an olive tree, that we dug it up.'

'So you were present at the find?'

'Yes, sir. Monsieur de Peyrehorade told Jean Coll and me, a fortnight ago, to uproot an old olive tree which had been killed by the frost last year, for there was a very hard frost, you'll remember. Well, then, while he was working at it with all his might, Jean Coll gave a blow with his pickaxe, and I heard a ting, just as if he had hit a bell. "What's that?" I said. We went on picking away, and a black hand appeared, which looked like the hand of a dead man coming out of the ground. I felt frightened; I went up to Monsieur and I said to him: "There's dead folk, master, under the olive tree; you'll have to send for the priest." "What dead folk?" he asked. He came along, and he'd no sooner seen the hand than he cried out: "An antique statue! An antique statue!" You might have thought he'd found buried treasure. And then he set to with a pickaxe and hands, as if his life depended on it, and did almost as much work as the two of us together.'

'And what did you find in the end?'

'A huge black woman, more than half naked, saving your

presence, sir, all in copper, and Monsieur de Peyrehorade told us it was an idol of pagan times ... you know, when Charlemagne was alive.'

'I see what it is ... a statue of the Virgin in bronze which belonged to a convent that has been destroyed.'

'The Blessed Virgin? Not on your life! ... I'd have known straight away if it had been the Blessed Virgin. I tell you it's an idol; you can see from her appearance. She looks straight at you with her great white eyes. ... Anybody'd think she was trying to stare you out, because you daren't look her in the eyes.'

'White eyes, were they? No doubt they are inlaid in the bronze; it might be a Roman statue.'

'Roman! That's it! Monsieur de Peyrehorade said that it was Roman. Ah! I can see that you're a learned man like him.'

'Is it whole and in good condition?'

'Oh, it's all there, Monsieur. It's much more beautiful and better finished than the painted plaster bust of Louis-Philippe in the town hall. But for all that, I don't fancy the idol's face. She looks wicked ... and she is wicked, too.'

'Wicked! What harm has she done you?'

'None to me exactly; but you can judge for yourself. We had gone down on all fours to raise her up on end, and Monsieur de Peyrehorade, too, was tugging at the rope, although he's no stronger than a chicken, the dear man! After a lot of trouble we got her upright. I was picking up a tile to prop her up, when—bang!—she fell slap on her back. "Look out!" I yelled, but I wasn't quick enough, for Jean Coll didn't have time to pull his leg away.'

'And was he injured?'

'His poor leg was broken as clean as a whistle. By heavens, when I saw it I was furious. I wanted to break up the idol with my pickaxe, but Monsieur de Peyrehorade wouldn't let me. He gave some money to Jean Coll, but all the same, he's been in bed the whole fortnight since it happened, and the doctor says he'll never walk with that leg again as well as

B

with the other. It's a crying shame; he was our best runner and, after Monsieur de Peyrehorade's son, our best tennis player too. Monsieur Alphonse de Peyrehorade was terribly upset, for he always played against Coll. It was a treat to see them sending the balls back and forth. Biff! Biff! They never touched the ground.'

Chatting like this, we reached Ille, and I soon found myself in the presence of Monsieur de Peyrehorade. He was a little old man, still spry and active; he had powdered hair, a red nose, and a jovial, bantering manner. Before opening Monsieur de P.'s letter he had installed me at a well-appointed table and presented me to his wife and son as a famous archaeologist, who was going to raise the province of Roussillon from the obscurity in which it had been left by the neglect of the learned.

While I was eating with a good appetite—for nothing makes one so hungry as mountain air—I examined my hosts. I have said a word or two about Monsieur de Peyrehorade; I should add that he was vivacity itself. He talked and ate, got up, ran to his library, brought me books, showed me engravings, and poured out drinks for me; he was never still for two minutes at a time. His wife was rather too stout, like most Catalan women over forty, and she seemed to me an out-and-out provincial, completely taken up with the cares of her household. Although the supper was ample for six people at least, she ran to the kitchen, had scores of pigeons killed and fried, and opened heaven knows how many pots of preserves. In a trice the table was littered with dishes and bottles, and I should undoubtedly have died of indigestion if I had so much as tasted all that was offered me. However, at each dish that I refused there were fresh apologies. They were afraid I would be very badly off at Ille—they had so few resources in the provinces, and Parisians were so hard to please!

Monsieur Alphonse de Peyrehorade stirred no more than a statue in the midst of his parents' comings and goings. He was a tall young man of twenty-six, with handsome, regular

features, but which were lacking in expression. His figure
and his athletic build fully justified the reputation he had
enjoyed in the region as an indefatigable tennis player. That
evening he was exquisitely dressed, just like the latest
fashion plate. But he seemed to me to be ill at ease in his
garments; he was as stiff as a post in his velvet collar, and
did not turn round unless all of a piece. His large sunburnt
hands, with their short nails, contrasted strangely with his
costume. They were the hands of a ploughman poking out
of the sleeves of a dandy. For the rest, although he studied
me from head to foot very inquisitively in my capacity as
a Parisian, he only spoke to me once in the whole evening,
and that was to ask me where I had bought my watch-
chain.

'Ah, now, my honoured guest,' Monsieur de Peyrehorade
said to me when supper was drawing to its conclusion, 'you
belong to me. You are in my house and I shall not give you
any peace until you have seen everything of any interest
among our mountains. You must learn to know our Roussillon and to do it justice. You have no idea what we can show
you—Phoenician, Celtic, Roman, Arab, and Byzantine
monuments. You shall see them all—lock, stock, and barrel.
I shall take you everywhere, and I shan't spare you a single
stone.'

A fit of coughing compelled him to stop. I took advantage
of it to tell him I should be greatly distressed if I disturbed
him during the important event about to take place in his
family. If he would be so kind as to give me the benefit of
his valuable advice about the outings I ought to go on, then
without putting him to the inconvenience of accompanying
me, I would be able to . . .

'Ah, you're referring to this young fellow's marriage!' he
exclaimed, interrupting me. 'That's nothing. It takes place
the day after tomorrow. You shall celebrate the wedding
with us; it will be a quiet affair, for the bride is in mourning
for an aunt, whose heiress she is. So there won't be any
festivities, and there won't be a ball. . . . That's a pity. . . .

You would have seen our Catalan women dance. . . . They're very pretty, and you might have been tempted to follow Alphonse's example. One marriage, they say, leads to others. . . . On Saturday, after the young people are married, I shall be at liberty, and we'll set out. I must apologize for boring you with a provincial wedding. To a Parisian who has had his fill of festivities . . . And a wedding without a ball too! However, you will see a bride . . . a bride . . . who will take your breath away. . . . But you are a serious man, and you are no longer interested in women. I have better things to show you. I'm going to give you something to feast your eyes on! I've a fine surprise in store for you tomorrow.'

'Ah,' I replied, 'it isn't easy to have a treasure in your house without the public knowing about it. I think I can guess the surprise you have in store for me. If it's your statue you're talking about, I'm quite prepared to admire it, for my guide's description of it has whetted my curiosity.'

'Ah, so he's told you about the idol, for that is what they call my beautiful Venus Tur—but I refuse to say another word. Tomorrow, as soon as it is daylight, you shall see her, and you shall tell me if I am not right in considering her a masterpiece. Upon my word, you couldn't have arrived at a better time! There are inscriptions which I in my ignorance explain as best I can . . . but a scholar from Paris! . . . You'll probably laugh at my interpretation, for I have written a treatise on it. . . . I—an old provincial antiquarian—I've been so bold . . . I want to set the press groaning. If you would be so good as to read and correct it, I might hope . . . For example, I would very much like to know how you would translate this inscription on the pedestal: 'CAVE. . . .' But I don't want to ask you anything yet! Tomorrow, tomorrow! Not a word about the Venus today.'

'You're quite right, Peyrehorade,' said his wife, 'to stop talking about your idol. You ought to see that you're preventing our guest from eating. Why, he has seen far more beautiful statues in Paris than yours. There are dozens of them in the Tuileries, and in bronze too.'

'Now there's ignorance for you—the blessed ignorance of the provinces!' interrupted Monsieur de Peyrehorade. 'Fancy comparing a splendid antique statute to the mediocre figures of Coustou!

> How irreverently of the gods
> My wife is pleased to talk!

'Do you know my wife wanted me to have my statue melted down to make a bell for our church? She would have been its godmother. A masterpiece of Myron's, Monsieur!'

'A masterpiece! A masterpiece! A fine masterpiece it is to break a man's leg!'

'Look here, wife,' said Monsieur de Peyrehorade in a determined voice, as he stretched his right leg out towards her, clad in a shadowed silk stocking, 'if my Venus had broken this leg I wouldn't have complained.'

'Good gracious! Peyrehorade, how can you say a thing like that? Fortunately, the man is getting better. . . . All the same, I can't bring myself to look at a statue which did a dreadful thing like that. Poor Jean Coll!'

'Wounded by Venus, Monsieur', said Monsieur de Peyrehorade, laughing loudly. 'The rascal complains of being wounded by Venus!

> Veneris nec praemia nôris.

Who hasn't been wounded by Venus in his time?'

Monsieur Alphonse, who understood French better than Latin, gave a knowing wink, and looked at me as if to say: 'Do you understand that, you Parisian?'

Supper came to an end. For an hour I had not been able to eat any more. I was tired, and I could not manage to hide my frequent yawns. Madame de Peyrehorade was the first to notice and said that it was time to retire. Then began fresh apologies for the poor bed I was going to have. I would not be as comfortable as I was in Paris; in the country things were so inferior. I must make allowances for the people of

Roussillon. It was in vain I protested that after a journey among the mountains a bundle of straw would seem a wonderful bed: they still begged me to pardon poor country folk if they did not treat me as well as they would have wished. At last, accompanied by Monsieur de Peyrehorade, I reached the room prepared for me. The staircase, the top steps of which were of wood, led to the centre of a corridor, off which several rooms opened.

'To the right', said my host, 'is the set of rooms I intend for the future Madame Alphonse. Your room is at the other end of the corridor. You will understand,' he added, with a look which he meant to be sly, 'you will readily understand that newly married people have to be isolated. You are at one end of the house and they at the other.'

We entered a handsomely furnished room, where the first object which met my eye was a bed seven feet long, six feet wide, and so high that one needed a stool to get into it. My host pointed out the position of the bell, and after making sure that the sugar-bowl was full, and the bottles of eau-de-Cologne in their proper places on the dressing-table, and asking me several times if I had all I wanted, wished me good night and left me alone.

The windows were shut. Before undressing, I opened one to breathe the cool night air, which was delicious after such a lengthy supper. In front was the Canigou, which is always a wonderful sight, but which that night struck me as the most beautiful mountain in the world, lighted up as it was by a splendid moon. I stood for a few minutes contemplating its marvellous outline, and I was just going to close my window when, lowering my gaze, I saw the statue on a pedestal about forty yards from the house. It had been placed at a corner of the quickset hedge which separated a little garden from a large, perfectly level, square plot which, I learnt later, was the town tennis court. This ground had been Monsieur de Peyrehorade's property, but he had given it to the public at his son's urgent request.

From where I was, it was difficult for me to make out the

posture of the statue; I could only judge its height, which I guessed was about six feet. At that moment two town rowdies passed along the tennis court, close to the hedge, whistling the pretty Roussillon tune, *Montagnes régalades*. They stopped to look at the statue, and one of them even apostrophized her in a loud voice. He spoke the Catalan dialect, but I had been long enough in the province of Roussillon to be able to understand nearly all that he said.

'So there you are, you hussy!' (The Catalan expression was more forcible than that.) 'There you are', he said. 'So it was you as broke Jean Coll's leg! If you belonged to me I'd break your neck.'

'Bah! What with?' asked the other. 'She's made of copper, and so hard that Étienne broke his file on her, trying to cut into her. It's copper from pagan times, and harder than anything I can think of.'

'If I had my cold chisel' (apparently he was a locksmith's apprentice), 'I'd soon knock out her big white eyes; it would be like getting a couple of almonds out of their shells. There's over five francs' worth of silver in them.'

They moved a few paces farther off.

'I must wish the idol good night', said the taller of the apprentices, stopping suddenly.

He stooped, and probably picked up a stone. I saw him stretch out his arm and throw something, and immediately after, I heard a loud noise come from the bronze. At the same moment the apprentice raised his hand to his head and cried out in pain.

'She's thrown it back at me!' he exclaimed.

And the two scamps took to their heels as fast as they could. The stone had obviously rebounded from the metal, and had punished the rascal for the outrage done to the goddess.

I shut the window, laughing heartily.

'Yet another vandal punished by Venus! Would that all destroyers of our ancient monuments could have their heads broken like that!'

And with this charitable wish I fell asleep.

It was broad daylight when I awoke. On one side of the bed stood Monsieur de Peyrehorade in a dressing-gown; on the other, a servant sent by his wife with a cup of chocolate in his hand.

'Come now, Parisian, get up! How lazy you people from the capital are!' said my host, while I hurriedly dressed. 'It's eight o'clock and here you are, still in bed. I've been up since six o'clock. I've been upstairs three times; I've tiptoed up to your door; but there was no sign of life at all. It is bad for you to sleep too much at your age. And my Venus waiting to be seen! Come along, drink this cup of Barcelona chocolate as fast as you can. . . . It's real contraband. You can't get chocolate like this in Paris. Take in all the nourishment you can, for when you see my Venus, no one will be able to tear you away.'

I was ready in five minutes, that is to say, I was only half shaved, carelessly buttoned, and scalded by the chocolate which I had swallowed boiling hot. I went down into the garden and soon found myself in front of an admirable statue.

It was indeed a Venus, and one of extraordinary beauty. The upper part of her body was bare, just as the ancients usually depicted their great deities; her right hand, raised to the level of her breast, was turned palm inwards, the thumb and two first fingers extended, while the other two were slightly curved. The other hand was near the hips, and held up the drapery which covered the lower part of the body. The attitude of this statue reminded me of that of the Morra player, which, for some reason or other, goes by the name of Germanicus. Perhaps the sculptor wished to depict the goddess playing the game of Morra.

However that might be, it is impossible to imagine anything more perfect than the body of that Venus; nothing could be more harmonious or more voluptuous than her outlines, nothing more graceful or dignified than her drapery. I had expected some work of the Later Empire, and I was confronted with a masterpiece of the most perfect period of sculpture. What struck me most of all was the exquisite truth of form, which might have led one to suppose that it had been moulded by nature herself, if nature ever produced such perfect specimens.

The hair, which was raised off the forehead, looked as if it had been gilded at some time. The head was small, like those of nearly all Greek statues, and bent slightly forward. As for the face, I should never be able to express its strange character; it was of quite a different type from that of any other antique statue I could remember. It was not at all the calm and austere beauty of the Greek sculptors, whose rule was to give a majestic immobility to every feature. Here, on the contrary, I noticed with astonishment that the artist had deliberately set out to express ill-nature raised to the level of wickedness. Every feature was slightly contracted: the eyes were rather slanted, the mouth turned up at the corners, and the nostrils somewhat distended. Disdain, irony, cruelty, could be distinguished in that face which was, notwithstanding, of incredible beauty. Indeed, the longer one looked at that wonderful statue, the more distress one felt at the thought that such a marvellous beauty could be united with an utter absence of goodness.

'If the model ever existed,' I said to Monsieur de Peyrehorade, 'and I doubt if Heaven ever produced such a woman, how I pity her lovers! She must have delighted in making them die of despair. There is something ferocious in her expression, and yet I have never seen anything so beautiful.'

> 'Venus with all her might has fastened
>   on her prey',

exclaimed Monsieur de Peyrehorade, pleased with my enthusiasm.

That expression of fiendish scorn was perhaps enhanced by the contrast offered by her eyes, which were encrusted with silver and shone brightly, with the greenish-black patina which time had given to the whole statue. Those bright eyes produced a kind of illusion which recalled real life. I remembered what my guide had said, that she made those who looked at her lower their eyes. That was almost true, and I could hardly restrain an impulse of anger with myself for feeling rather ill at ease before that bronze face.

'Now that you have admired it in detail, my dear colleague in antiquarian research,' said my host, 'let us, by your leave, open a scientific conference. What do you think about this inscription, which you haven't noticed yet?'

He showed me the pedestal of the statue, and I read on it these words:

CAVE AMANTEM

'*Quid dicis, doctissime?*' he asked me, rubbing his hands together. 'Let us see if we agree on the meaning of this *cave amantem.*'

'But', I answered, 'it has two meanings. It can be translated: "Beware of him who loves thee; mistrust thy lovers." But in that sense I don't know whether *cave amantem* would be good Latin. Looking at the lady's diabolical expression, I would rather think that the artist intended to put the spectator on his guard against her terrible beauty; I would therefore translate it: "Beware if she loves thee." '

'Humph!' said Monsieur de Peyrehorade; 'yes, that is an admissible interpretation; but, with all respect, I prefer the first translation, and I will tell you why. You know who Venus's lover was?'

'There were several.'

'Yes, but the chief one was Vulcan. Didn't the sculptor mean: "In spite of all thy beauty and thy scornful expression, thou shalt have for thy lover a blacksmith, an ugly cripple"? What a profound lesson, Monsieur, for flirts!'

I could hardly help smiling at this far-fetched explanation.

'Latin is a difficult tongue, because of its conciseness', I remarked, to avoid contradicting my antiquarian friend outright; and I stepped back a few paces to see the statue better.

'One moment, colleague,' said Monsieur de Peyrehorade,

seizing me by the arm, 'you haven't seen everything. There is another inscription. Climb up on the pedestal and look at the right arm.' And saying this, he helped me up.

I held on rather unceremoniously to the Venus's neck, and began to make myself better acquainted with her. I even looked at her right in the face for a moment, and found her even more spiteful and beautiful at close quarters. Then I discovered that there were some written characters, in what seemed to me an ancient, running hand, engraved on the arm. With the help of my spectacles I spelt out the following, while Monsieur de Peyrehorade repeated every word as soon as I uttered it, with approving gestures and voice. It read thus:

> *VENERI TVRBVL...*
> *EVTYCHES MYRO*
> *IMPERIO FECIT.*

After the word *TVRBVL* in the first line, I thought that there were some letters which had been effaced; but *TVRBVL* was perfectly legible.

'What does that mean?' asked my gleeful host, mischievously smiling, for he knew very well that I would not find it easy to make much of this *TVRBVL*.

'There is one thing which I cannot explain yet', I said to him; 'all the rest is easy. Eutyches Myron made this offering to Venus by her order.'

'Good. But what do you make of *TVRBVL*? What is *TVRBVL*?'

'*TVRBVL* puzzles me greatly; I cannot think of any epithet normally applied to Venus which might assist me. Let us see: what would you say to *TVRBVLENTA*? Venus who troubles and disturbs. . . . You notice I am still preoccupied with her spiteful expression. *TVRBVLENTA* is not at all a bad epithet for Venus', I added modestly, for I myself was not quite satisfied with my explanation.

'Venus the turbulent! Venus the disturber! Ah! So you think that my Venus is a Venus of the pot-house? Nothing of the sort, Monsieur. She is a Venus of good society. And now I will explain this *TVRBVL* to you. You will at least promise not to divulge my discovery before my treatise is published. I am rather proud, you see, of this find. . . . You really must leave us poor provincial devils a few ears to glean. You Parisian savants are rich enough.'

From the top of the pedestal, where I was still perched, I solemnly promised that I would never be so dishonourable as to steal his discovery.

'For *TVRBVL*, Monsieur,' he said, coming nearer and lowering his voice for fear that anyone else but myself might hear, 'read *TVRBVLNERAE.*'

'I don't understand any better.'

'Listen carefully. A league from here, at the foot of the mountain, there is a village called Boulternère. That is a corruption of the Latin word *TVRBVLNERA*. Nothing is commoner than such an inversion. Boulternère, Monsieur, was a Roman town. I had always thought so, but I had never had any proof of it. The proof lies here. This Venus was the local goddess of the city of Boulternère; and this word Boulternère, which I have just shown to be of ancient origin, proves a still more curious thing, namely, that Boulternère, after being a Roman town, became a Phoenician one!'

He stopped a minute to take breath, and to enjoy my surprise. I had to repress a strong inclination to laugh.

'Indeed,' he went on, '*TVRBVLNERA* is pure Phoenician. *TVR* can be pronounced *TOUR*. . . . *TOUR* and *SOUR* are the same word, are they not? *SOUR* is the Phoenician name for Tyre. I need not remind you of its meaning. *BVL* is Baal, Bâl, Bel, Bul, slight differences in pronunciation. As for *NERA*, that gives me some trouble. I am tempted to think, for want of a Phoenician word, that it comes from the Greek νηρός—damp, marshy. That would make it a hybrid word. To justify νηρός I will show you at Boulternère how the mountain streams there form foul pools. On the other hand, the ending *NERA* might have been added much later, in honour of Nera Pivesuvia, the wife of Tetricus, who may have rendered some service to the city of Turbul. But, on account of the pools, I prefer the derivation from νηρός.'

He took a pinch of snuff with a satisfied air.

'But let us leave the Phoenicians and return to the inscription. I translate, then: "To the Venus of Boulternère Myron dedicates at her command this statue, the work of his hand." '

I took good care not to criticize his etymology, but I wanted, in my turn, to give some proof of perspicacity, so I said to him:

'Wait a bit, Monsieur. Myron dedicated something, but I don't in the least see that it was this statue.'

'What!' he exclaimed. 'Wasn't Myron a famous Greek sculptor? The talent would pass on to his descendants; and one of them made this statue. Nothing can be clearer.'

'But', I replied, 'I see a little hole in the arm. I fancy it has been used to fasten something, perhaps a bracelet, which this Myron gave to Venus as an expiatory offering, for Myron was an unlucky lover. Venus was angry with him, and he appeased her by consecrating a golden bracelet. You must remember that *fecit* is often used for *consecravit*. The terms are synonymous. I could show you more than one instance if I had access to Gruter or, better still, Orelli. It is natural that a lover should see Venus in his dreams, and that he should imagine that she ordered him to give her statue a golden bracelet. Myron consecrated a bracelet to her. . . . Then the barbarians, or perhaps some sacrilegious thief. . . .'

'Ah, it's easy to see that you have written some novels', exclaimed my host, helping me down. 'No, Monsieur, it is a work of Myron's school. Just look at the workmanship, and you'll agree.'

Having made it a rule never to contradict pig-headed antiquarians outright, I bowed my head as if convinced, and said: 'It's a splendid piece of work.'

'Good gracious!' exclaimed Monsieur de Peyrehorade, 'here's another piece of vandalism! Someone has thrown a stone at my statue!'

He had just noticed a white mark a little above the breast of the Venus. I saw a similar mark on the fingers of the right hand, which I then supposed had been touched by the stone in passing, or else a fragment of it might have been broken off by the shock and hit the hand. I told my host about the insult I had witnessed and the prompt punishment which had followed. He laughed heartily, and compared the apprentice to Diomedes, expressing the hope that he would see all his comrades changed into white birds, as the Greek hero did.

The breakfast bell interrupted this classical conversation; and, as on the previous evening, I was forced to eat as much as four people. Then Monsieur de Peyrehorade's tenants came to see him, and, while he was giving them audience, his son took me to see a carriage which he had bought for his fiancée at Toulouse, and which I naturally admired. After that I went with him to the stables, where he kept me for half an hour praising his horses, telling me their pedigrees, and listing the prizes he had won at the country races. At last he spoke of his future bride, in connexion with a grey mare which he intended to give her.

'We shall see her today. I don't know if you will think her pretty. You are so hard to please in Paris; but everybody here and at Perpignan thinks her lovely. The best of it is she's very rich. Her aunt, who lived at Prades, left her all her money. Oh, I'm going to be ever so happy!'

I was deeply shocked to see a young man appear more affected by the dowry than by the beauty of his bride-to-be.

'Do you know anything about jewellery?' continued Monsieur Alphonse. 'What do you think of this ring which I'm going to give her tomorrow?'

As he said this, he drew from the first joint of his little finger a large ring blazing with diamonds, and formed with two clasped hands: a most poetic conceit, I thought. It was of ancient workmanship, but I guessed that it had been retouched when the diamonds were set. Inside the ring was engraved in gothic letters: '*Sempr' ab ti*' ('Ever thine').

'It is a pretty ring', I said, but added: 'The diamonds have detracted slightly from its original character.'

'Oh, it's much prettier as it is now', he replied with a smile. 'There are one thousand two hundred francs' worth of diamonds in it. My mother gave it to me. It was an old family ring . . . from the days of chivalry. It was worn by my grandmother, who had it from her grandmother. Goodness knows when it was made!'

'The custom in Paris', I said, 'is to give a perfectly plain ring, usually made of two different metals, such as gold and platinum. For instance, the other ring which you have on that finger would be most suitable. This one is so large, with its diamonds and its hands in relief, that no glove would go over it.'

'Oh, Madame Alphonse can do as she likes. I think that she will be glad to have it in any case. Twelve hundred francs on one's finger is very pleasing. That little ring', he added, looking with a satisfied expression at the plain ring which he was holding, 'was given me one Shrove Tuesday by a woman in Paris. Ah, what a time I had when I was staying there two years ago. That's the place to enjoy oneself, and no mistake! . . .' And he sighed regretfully.

We were to dine at Puygarrig that day, at the house of the bride's parents; we drove over to the château, which was about a league and a half from Ille. I was introduced and received as a friend of the family. I will not talk of the dinner, nor of the conversation which followed, and in which I took little part. Monsieur Alphonse, who was seated next to his future bride, whispered in her ear every quarter of an hour. As for her, she hardly raised her eyes, and blushed modestly every time her intended spoke to her, though she replied without embarrassment.

Mademoiselle de Puygarrig was eighteen years old, and her lithe, delicate figure was a great contrast to the bony frame of her sturdy fiancé. She was not just beautiful: she was enchanting. I admired the perfect naturalness of all her replies. Her expression was kindly, but nevertheless was not devoid of a slight touch of maliciousness which reminded me, in spite of myself, of my host's Venus. While making this comparison to myself, I wondered if the superior beauty which the statue undoubtedly possessed was not largely due to her tigerish expression, for strength, even in the evil passions, always arouses wonder and a sort of involuntary admiration.

What a pity, I reflected, as we left Puygarrig, that such a charming person should be so rich, and that her dowry should be the cause of her being courted by a man unworthy of her!

On the way back to Ille, not knowing what to talk about to Madame de Peyrehorade, but thinking I ought to speak to her, I said:

'You are very sceptical folk here in Roussillon, to have a wedding on a Friday. In Paris, we are more superstitious; nobody would dare to get married on that day.'

'Oh, please don't talk about it', she said; 'if it had depended only on me, I would certainly have chosen another day. But Peyrehorade wanted it, and I had to give in to him. It worries me, though. Suppose some misfortune should happen? There must be something in it, or else why should everybody be afraid of a Friday?'

'Friday', her husband exclaimed, 'is the day dedicated to Venus. An excellent day for a wedding. You will notice, my dear colleague, that I think of nothing but my Venus. Naturally, it was on her account that I chose a Friday. To-morrow, if you are willing, we will offer her a small sacrifice before the ceremony—two ring-doves and, if I can find any, some incense. . . .'

'For shame, Peyrehorade!' interrupted his wife, who was deeply shocked. 'Offer incense to an idol! It would be an outrage! What would people say about you round here?'

'At all events', said Monsieur de Peyrehorade, 'you will let me put a wreath of roses and lilies on her head.

Manibus date lilia plenis.

You see, Monsieur, the Charter is a vain thing. We have no religious freedom.'

The arrangements for the next day were made in the following manner. Everyone had to be ready and dressed for the wedding at ten o'clock sharp. After taking chocolate we were to drive over to Puygarrig. The civil marriage was to take place at the village registry, and the religious ceremony in the château chapel. After that there would be a luncheon. Then we would be able to spend the time as we liked until seven o'clock, when we were all to return to Monsieur de Peyrehorade's house, where the two families would have supper together. The rest followed naturally. Since there could be no dancing, it had been decided to have as much eating as possible.

As early as eight o'clock, I was sitting in front of the Venus, pencil in hand, beginning again for the twentieth time the statue's head, without being able to seize the expression. Monsieur de Peyrehorade bustled about, giving me advice and repeating his Phoenician derivations. Then he placed some Bengal roses on the pedestal of the statue and addressed to it, in a tragi-comical voice, supplications for the couple who were going to live under his roof. He went in to change about nine o'clock, and at the same time Monsieur Alphonse appeared, wearing a close-fitting suit, white gloves, patent-leather shoes, chased buttons, and a rose in his buttonhole.

'You must do my wife's portrait', he said, leaning over my drawing; 'she is pretty, too.'

Just then, on the tennis court which I have already mentioned, a game started that at once attracted Monsieur Alphonse's attention. I was tired and, despairing of being able to reproduce that diabolical face, I soon left my drawing to watch the players. There were among them a few Spanish muleteers who had arrived the night before. They were men from Aragon and from Navarre, almost all remarkable players. Although the local players were encouraged by the presence and advice of Monsieur Alphonse, they were very

C

soon beaten by these new champions. The patriotic on-
lookers were aghast. Monsieur Alphonse looked at his watch.
It was still only half past nine. His mother was not ready yet.
He hesitated no longer, threw off his coat, asked for a jacket,
and challenged the Spaniards. I looked at him with amusement and in some surprise.

'The honour of our country must be upheld', he
said.

At that moment I admired him. His blood was up. His
clothes, which a little earlier had filled his thoughts to the
exclusion of everything else, were completely forgotten. A
few minutes before he would not have dared turn his head,
for fear of disturbing his cravat. Now he no longer gave a
thought to his curled hair or his beautifully pleated jabot.
As for his fiancée, I do believe that, if necessary, he would
have postponed the wedding. I saw him hastily put on a
pair of sandals, roll up his sleeves, and with a confident
air put himself at the head of the defeated side, like Caesar
when he rallied his soldiers at Dyrrachium. I jumped over
the hedge and took up a convenient position in the shade
of a nettle tree in such a way as to be able to see both
sides.

Contrary to general expectation, Monsieur Alphonse
missed the first ball; true, it grazed the ground, hit with
astonishing force by one of the players from Aragon, who
seemed to be the leader of the Spaniards.

He was a man of about forty, six feet tall, slim and wiry;
and his olive skin was almost as dark as the bronze of the
Venus.

Monsieur Alphonse threw his racquet on the ground in a
rage.

'It's this damned ring', he exclaimed, 'which is too tight
on my finger and made me miss a sure thing.'

With some difficulty he took off his diamond ring, and I
went over to him to take it, but he forestalled me, ran to the
Venus, slipped the ring on her third finger, and resumed his
position at the head of his fellow villagers.

He was pale, but calm and determined. From then on he made no more mistakes, and the Spaniards were soundly beaten. The enthusiasm of the spectators was a fine sight: some uttered shrieks of joy and threw their caps in the air; others shook hands with him and called him the pride of the region. If he had repulsed an invasion I doubt if he would have received heartier or more sincere congratulations. The disappointment of the vanquished added still more to the splendour of his victory.

'We must have another match, my good fellow', he said to the muleteer from Aragon in a condescending tone; 'but I must give you points.'

I would have preferred Monsieur Alphonse to be more modest, and I was almost sorry for his rival's humiliation.

The Spanish giant felt the insult keenly. I saw him go pale under his tanned skin. He looked miserably at his racquet and ground his teeth; then in a choking voice he muttered: 'Me lo pagarás.'[1]

The voice of Monsieur de Peyrehorade interrupted his son's triumph; my host was astonished not to find him superintending the preparation of the new carriage, and even more astonished to see him holding a racquet and dripping with sweat.

Monsieur Alphonse ran to the house, washed his face and hands, put on his new coat again and his patent-leather shoes, and five minutes later we were in full trot on the road to Puygarrig. All the tennis players of the town and a large crowd of spectators followed us with shouts of joy. The stout horses which drew us could only just keep ahead of those dauntless Catalans.

We had reached Puygarrig, and the procession was about to set off for the village hall when Monsieur Alphonse suddenly slapped his forehead, and whispered to me:

'What a blunder! I've forgotten the ring! It's on the Venus's finger, damn her! Don't tell my mother, whatever happens. Perhaps she won't notice anything.'

[1] 'You'll pay for this.'

'You could send someone for it', I said.

'No. My servant has stayed behind at Ille, and I can't trust these fellows here. There's more than one of them who might be tempted by twelve hundred francs' worth of diamonds. Besides, what would the people here think of my absent-mindedness? They'd make fun of me and call me the statue's husband. . . . If only nobody steals it! Fortunately, the idol frightens the young rascals. They daren't go within arm's length of her. Well, it doesn't matter. I have another ring.'

The two ceremonies, civil and religious, were performed with suitable pomp. Mademoiselle de Puygarrig received the ring of a Paris milliner, little thinking that her fiancé had sacrificed a love-token to her. Then we sat down and drank, ate, and sang for long enough. I felt sorry for the bride, who had to put up with the coarse jollity which was going on all around her; however, she took it better than I would have thought possible, and her embarrassment was neither awkward nor affected. Perhaps courage comes to people in difficult situations.

The luncheon eventually came to an end, and at four o'clock the men went for a walk in the park, which was a magnificent one, or watched the peasant girls of Puygarrig dance on the château lawn, dressed in their best clothes. We spent a few hours like this. In the meantime the women crowded round the bride, who showed them her wedding presents. Then she changed, and I noticed that she covered up her beautiful hair with a cap and a hat with feathers in it, for women are always in a hurry to don as quickly as possible those adornments which custom forbids them to wear while they are still unmarried.

It was nearly eight o'clock when we made ready to go back to Ille. But first a pathetic scene took place. Mademoiselle de Puygarrig's aunt, who had been a mother to her, a lady of advanced age and very religious, was not due to come to Ille with us. On our departure she gave her niece a touching sermon on her wifely duties, which resulted in a

flood of tears and endless embraces. Monsieur de Peyrehorade compared this parting to the Rape of the Sabines.
However, we set off at last, and during the journey everyone
did their utmost to cheer up the bride and make her laugh,
but in vain.

At Ille supper was waiting for us; and what a supper! If
the morning's coarse jollity had shocked me, I was even
more disgusted by the quips and jokes of which bride and
bridegroom were the chief butts. The bridegroom, who had
disappeared for a moment before sitting down to supper,
was as pale and chilly as an iceberg. He kept drinking the
old wine of Collioure, which is almost as strong as brandy.
I was sitting beside him, and felt I ought to warn him:

'Have a care. They say that wine . . .'

I don't know what nonsense I said to him to put myself
in unison with the other guests.

He nudged my knee and whispered:

'When we get up from the table I have something to say
to you.'

His solemn tone surprised me. I looked at him more
closely, and noticed a strange alteration in his features.

'Do you feel ill?' I asked.

'No.'

And he started drinking again.

In the meantime, in the midst of all the shouting and
clapping of hands, a child of eleven, who had slipped under
the table, showed the company a pretty white and pink
ribbon which he had just taken from the bride's ankle. They
called it her garter. It was promptly cut and distributed
among the young people, who decorated their buttonholes
with it, in accordance with a very old custom which is still
observed in a few patriarchal families. This made the bride
blush to the whites of her eyes. But her confusion reached
its height when Monsieur de Peyrehorade, after calling for
silence, sang some Catalan verses to her, which he said were
impromptu. This is the meaning, so far as I understand it.

'What is the matter with me, my friends? Has the wine

I have drunk made me see double? There are two Venuses here. . . .'

The bridegroom turned round suddenly with a frightened expression, which set everybody laughing.

'Yes,' continued Monsieur de Peyrehorade, 'there are two Venuses under my roof. One I found in the earth, like a truffle; the other came down to us from the heavens to share her girdle with us.'

He meant, of course, her garter.

'My son chose between the Roman and the Catalan Venus. The rascal chooses the Catalan, the better part, for the Roman is black and the Catalan is white; the Roman is cold, and the Catalan sets on fire all who come near her.'

This conclusion aroused such an uproar of noisy applause and loud laughter that I thought the roof would fall on our heads. There were only three grave faces at the table—those of the bridal couple and mine. I had a splitting headache; besides, I don't know why, a wedding always makes me feel melancholy. This one disgusted me slightly too.

The last couplets were sung by the deputy mayor, and, I must say, they were very broad; then we went into the drawing-room to witness the departure of the bride, who was soon to be conducted to her bedroom, as it was nearly midnight.

Monsieur Alphonse drew me aside into the recess of a window, and, turning his eyes away, said to me:

'You will laugh at me . . . but I don't know what is the matter with me . . . I am bewitched, dammit!'

My first thought was that he fancied he was threatened with some misfortune of the sort referred to by Montaigne and Madame de Sévigné: 'The whole realm of love is full of tragic stories.'

'I thought that this kind of mishap only happened to men of genius', I said to myself.

'You have drunk too much Collioure wine, my dear Monsieur Alphonse', I said. 'I did warn you.'

'That may be. But this is something much worse.'

His voice was broken, and I thought he was quite drunk.
'You know my ring?' he continued, after a pause.
'Yes. Has it been taken?'
'No.'
'In that case you have it?'
'No—I—I could not get it off the finger of that confounded Venus.'
'Nonsense! You didn't pull hard enough.'
'Yes, I did.... But the Venus ... has clenched her finger.'

He looked at me fixedly with a haggard expression, leaning against the window-latch to keep himself from falling.

'What a ridiculous tale!' I said. 'You pushed the ring too far. Tomorrow you must use pincers, only be careful not to injure the statue.'

'No, I tell you. The Venus's finger has contracted and bent up; she has closed her hand, do you hear? ... She's my wife, apparently, because I gave her my ring.... She won't give it back.'

I shivered suddenly, and for a moment my blood ran cold. Then a deep sigh he gave sent a breath of wine into my face and all my emotion disappeared.

'The wretch is completely drunk', I thought.

'You are an antiquarian, Monsieur', the bridegroom added in dismal tones; 'you know all about such statues.... There may be some spring, some devilish trick, I don't know about. If you would go and see....'

'Willingly', I said. 'Come with me.'
'No, I would rather you went by yourself.'
I left the drawing-room.

The weather had changed during supper, and rain was beginning to fall heavily. I was going to ask for an umbrella, when I stopped short and reflected. 'I should be a fool', I said to myself, 'to go and verify the tale of a man who is drunk. Besides, perhaps he intended to play some stupid trick on me to amuse these country people; and the least that could happen to me would be that I should get wet through and catch a bad cold.'

I cast a glance at the dripping statue from the door, and went up to my room without returning to the drawing-room. I went to bed, but sleep was a long time coming. All the scenes that had occurred during the day returned to my mind. I thought of that beautiful, innocent young girl given up to a drunken brute. 'What an odious thing', I said to myself, 'is a marriage of convenience! A mayor puts on a tricolour sash, and a priest a stole, and the most innocent of girls may be handed over to the Minotaur. What can two beings who do not love each other say at such a moment, a moment which lovers would buy at the price of life itself? Can a woman ever love a man whom she has once seen behaving in a vulgar way? First impressions can never be obliterated, and I am certain Monsieur Alphonse will deserve to be hated.'

During my monologue, which I have considerably abridged, I had heard much coming and going about the house, doors opening and shutting and carriages driving away; then I thought I could hear the light steps of several women on the stairs going towards the end of the passage opposite my room. It was probably the procession leading the bride to bed. Then they went downstairs again, and Madame de Peyrehorade's door shut. 'How unhappy and ill at ease that poor girl must feel!' I said to myself. I tossed about in my bed in a bad temper. A bachelor cuts a poor figure in a house where there is a wedding going on.

Silence had reigned for some time when it was interrupted by heavy steps coming up the stairs. The wooden stairs creaked loudly.

'What a clumsy lout!' I cried. 'I bet he'll fall downstairs.'

Then all became quiet again. I took a book to change the course of my thoughts. It was a statistical report on the Department, embellished with a memoir by Monsieur de Peyrehorade on the druidical monuments in the *Arrondissement* of Prades. I dozed off at the third page.

I slept badly and awoke several times. It must have been five in the morning, and I had been awake for over twenty minutes when the cock began to crow. Dawn was about to break. Then I distinctly heard the same heavy steps and the same creaking of the stairs that I had heard before I went to sleep. This struck me as very strange. I tried in the midst of my yawning to guess why Monsieur Alphonse should rise so early; I could not think of any likely reason. I was going to close my eyes again when my attention was aroused once more by a strange stamping noise which was soon mingled with the ringing of bells and the banging of doors, after which I distinguished some confused cries.

'That drunkard must have set fire to the house!' I thought, jumping out of bed.

I dressed rapidly and went into the corridor. Cries and wails were coming from the opposite end, and one piercing cry sounded above all the others: 'My son! My son!' Obviously some accident had happened to Monsieur Alphonse. I ran to the bridal-chamber; it was full of people. The first sight which met my eyes was the young man, half dressed, stretched across the bed, the wood of which was broken. He was livid and motionless, and his mother was weeping and crying by his side. Monsieur de Peyrehorade was busy rubbing his son's temples with eau-de-Cologne and holding smelling salts under his nose. Alas, his son had been dead a long time. On a couch at the other end of the room, the bride was in the grip of terrible convulsions. She was uttering inarticulate cries, and two strapping servants were having the greatest difficulty in holding her down.

'Good God!' I exclaimed. 'What has happened?'

I went to the bedside and raised the body of the unfortunate young man; he was already cold and stiff. His clenched teeth and blackened face denoted the most frightful pain. It was obvious that his death had been violent and his agony terrible. There was, however, no trace of blood on his clothes. I opened his shirt and found a livid mark on his breast which extended down his sides and over his back. It was as if he had been crushed in a band of iron. My foot stepped on something hard which was lying on the rug; I bent down and saw the diamond ring.

I led Monsieur de Peyrehorade and his wife away into their room; then I had the bride carried there.

'You have a daughter left', I said to them; 'you must give all your care to her.' Then I left them to themselves.

There seemed to me to be no doubt that Monsieur Alphonse had been the victim of a murder, and that the murderers had found some means of entering the bride's room during the night. Those bruises, however, on the chest and their circular direction puzzled me greatly, for neither a stick nor an iron bar could have produced them. Suddenly I remembered having heard that in Valence hired assassins used long leather bags full of fine sand to crush the people whom they had been paid to kill. I immediately recalled the muleteer from Aragon and his threat, though I found it hard to believe that he could have taken such a terrible revenge for a light jest.

I went round the house, looking everywhere for traces of someone having broken in, but I found none whatever. I went down into the garden to see if the murderers had got in from there, but I could not find any definite clue. The previous night's rain had, moreover, so soaked the ground that it could not have retained a clear imprint. But I noticed several deep footmarks in the earth; they were in two contrary directions, but in the same line, beginning at the corner of the hedge next to the tennis court and ending at the front door of the house. These might have been the footmarks made by Monsieur Alphonse when he had gone to get his ring from the statue's finger. Moreover, the hedge at that spot was not as thick as it was elsewhere, and it must have been there that the murderers had got through it. Passing to and fro in front of the statue, I stopped for a moment to look at it. I must admit that I could not look at its expression of ironical malice without fear, and my head was so full of the ghastly scenes I had just witnessed that I felt as if I were looking at an infernal divinity gloating over the misfortune which had befallen the house.

I went back to my room and remained there until noon. Then I went down and asked for news of my host and hostess. They were a little calmer. Mademoiselle de Puygarrig—or rather Monsieur Alphonse's widow—had regained consciousness; she had even spoken to the public attorney of Perpignan, then at Ille on an official visit, and this magistrate had taken down her statement. He asked me for mine. I told him what I knew, and did not conceal my suspicions regarding the muleteer from Aragon. He gave orders for him to be arrested immediately.

'Have you learnt anything from Madame Alphonse?' I asked the magistrate, when my statement had been taken down and signed.

'That unfortunate young lady has gone mad', he said, with a sad smile. 'Mad, completely mad. This is what she told me:

'She had been in bed, she said, for a few minutes with the curtains drawn, when the bedroom door opened and someone came in. Madame Alphonse was lying on the inside of the bed, with her face turned to the wall. She did not stir, convinced that it was her husband. A moment later the bed creaked as though it were burdened with an enormous weight. She was terribly frightened, but did not dare to turn round. Five minutes, or perhaps ten—she could not tell how long—passed. Then she made an involuntary movement, or else the other person in the bed made one, and she felt the touch of something as cold as ice—those are her very words. She pressed herself to the wall, trembling in every limb. Shortly after, the door opened again, and someone entered, who said: "Good evening, my little wife", and a little later the curtains were drawn. She heard a stifled cry. The person who was in bed beside her sat up, and seemed to stretch out both arms in front. Then she turned her head . . . and saw, so she says, her husband on his knees by the bed, with his head on a level with the pillow, in the arms of a sort of greenish giant who was embracing him with all its might. She said—

and she repeated it to me over and over again, poor woman!
—she said that she recognized . . . can you guess? The bronze
Venus, Monsieur de Peyrehorade's statue. . . . Since it was
found here, everybody has been dreaming about it. But to
go on with the story of the poor mad girl, she lost consciousness at this sight, and probably she had lost her reason a
little earlier. She cannot say how long she remained in a
faint. When she came to, she saw the phantom again—or the
statue, as she persists in calling it—motionless, its legs and
the lower half of its body on the bed, the bust and arms
stretched out before it, and in its arms her lifeless husband.
A cock crew, and then the statue got out of the bed, dropped
the dead body, and went out. Madame Alphonse tugged at
the bell, and you know the rest.'

They brought in the Spaniard; he was calm, and defended
himself with great coolness and presence of mind. He did
not attempt to deny the remark I had heard; he explained it
by maintaining that he meant nothing by it, but that on the
following day, when he had had a rest, he would have won
a game of tennis against his victor. I remember that he
added:

'A native of Aragon, when he is insulted, does not wait for
the next day to take his revenge. If I had thought that
Monsieur Alphonse meant to insult me, I would have immediately stabbed him with my knife.'

His shoes were compared with the marks in the garden;
but they were much larger than the footprints.

Finally, the innkeeper with whom the man was staying
asserted that he had spent the whole night rubbing and
doctoring one of his sick mules.

Moreover, this man from Aragon was highly respected
and well known in the district, to which he came annually
to do business. He was therefore released with many
apologies.

I had nearly forgotten the deposition of a servant who had
been the last person to see Monsieur Alphonse alive. It
had been just as he was going upstairs to his wife, and he had

called the man and asked him in an anxious manner if he knew where I was. The servant had replied that he had not seen me. Then Monsieur Alphonse had heaved a sigh, and stood there for a moment in silence. Then he had said:

'Well, the devil must have carried him off too!'

I asked this man if Monsieur Alphonse had had his diamond ring on when he had spoken to him. The servant hesitated before he replied; then he said that he thought not, that at all events he had not paid any attention.

'If he had been wearing that ring', he added, correcting himself, 'I should certainly have noticed it, because I thought that he had given it to Madame Alphonse.'

While I was questioning this man I felt a little of the superstitious terror that Madame Alphonse's deposition had spread throughout the house. The magistrate looked at me and smiled, and I refrained from pressing the point.

A few hours after Monsieur Alphonse's funeral, I prepared to leave Ille. Monsieur de Peyrehorade's carriage was to take me to Perpignan. In spite of his feeble condition the poor old man insisted on accompanying me to the gate of his garden. We crossed the garden in silence, with him hardly able to drag himself along even with the help of my arm. Just as we were parting, I cast a last glance at the Venus. I could see that my host, although he did not share the terror and hatred which it inspired in the rest of his family, would want to get rid of an object which would otherwise be a constant reminder of a frightful misfortune. I intended to try and persuade him to give it to a museum. I was wondering how to broach the subject when Monsieur de Peyrehorade automatically turned his head in the direction in which he saw me gazing. He saw the statue, and immediately burst into tears. I embraced him and, without daring to say a single word, I got into the carriage.

Since my departure I have not heard of any fresh discovery being made to throw light on that mysterious catastrophe.

Monsieur de Peyrehorade died a few months after his son. In his will he bequeathed me his manuscripts, which some day I may publish. But I have not been able to find among them the treatise relating to the inscription on the Venus.

P.S. My friend Monsieur de P. has just written to me from Perpignan to tell me that the statue no longer exists. After her husband's death, the first thing Madame de Peyrehorade did was to have it melted down and made into a bell, and in this new form it is used in the church at Ille. But, adds Monsieur de P., it would seem that an evil fate pursues those who possess that piece of bronze. Since that bell began to ring in Ille, the vines have twice been frost-bitten.

1837

Mateo Falcone

COMING out of Porto-Vecchio, and turning northwest towards the centre of the island, the traveller in Corsica sees the ground rise fairly rapidly, and after three hours' walk along tortuous paths, strewn with large boulders and sometimes cut by ravines, he finds himself on the edge of a very extensive *maquis*, or open heath. This heath is the home of the Corsican shepherds, and the resort of all those who have come in conflict with the law. The Corsican peasant sets fire to a certain stretch of forest to save himself the trouble of manuring his lands: so much the worse if the flames spread farther than is needed; whatever happens, he is sure to have a good harvest by sowing on this ground, fertilized by the ashes of the trees which grew on it. When the ears of corn have been harvested—for the straw is left because it is too much trouble to gather—the roots which have remained in the earth without being burned, sprout, in the following spring, into very thick shoots, which, in a few years, reach to a height of seven or eight feet. It is this sort of underwood which is called a *maquis*. It is composed of different kinds of trees and shrubs mixed up and entangled in complete confusion. It is only axe in hand that man could open a way through, and there are *maquis* so dense and so thick that not even the wild sheep can penetrate them.

If you have killed a man, go into the *maquis* of Porto-Vecchio, with a good gun and powder and shot, and you will live there in safety. Do not forget to take a brown cloak, furnished with a hood, which will serve as both blanket and mattress. The shepherds will give you milk, cheese, and chestnuts, and you will have nothing to fear from the hand of the law, nor from the relatives of the dead man, except when you go down into the town to renew your stock of ammunition.

When I was in Corsica in 18—, Mateo Falcone's house was half a league from this *maquis*. He was a comparatively rich man for that country, living like a noble, that is to say, without doing anything, from the produce of his herds, which the shepherds, a sort of nomadic people, led to pasture here and there in the mountains. When I saw him, two years after the event which I am about to relate, he seemed to me to be about fifty years of age at the most. Imagine a small but robust man, with jet-black, curly hair, an aquiline nose, thin lips, large and piercing eyes, and a deeply tanned complexion. His skill in shooting was considered extraordinary, even in this country where there are so many crack shots. For example, Mateo would never fire at a sheep with swan-shot, but, at one hundred and twenty paces, he would fell it with a bullet in its head or shoulders, as he chose. He could use his gun at night as easily as by day, and I was told the following example of his skill, which may seem incredible to anyone who has not travelled in Corsica. A lighted candle would be placed behind a transparent piece of paper, as large as a plate, at a distance of eighty paces. He would take aim, then the candle would be extinguished, and a minute later, in complete darkness, he would fire, piercing the paper three times out of four.

With this conspicuous talent Mateo Falcone had earned a great reputation. He was said to be as good a friend as he was a dangerous enemy; in other respects he was obliging and gave alms, and he lived at peace with everybody in the district of Porto-Vecchio. But it was said that at Corte, where he had found his wife, he had very quickly freed himself of a rival reputed to be equally formidable in love as in war; at any rate, people attributed to Mateo a certain shot which surprised his rival while in the act of shaving before a small mirror hanging on his window. After the affair had been more or less forgotten, Mateo married. His wife Giuseppa first presented him with three daughters, which enraged him, but finally a son came, whom he named Fortunato; he was the hope of the family, the heir to its name. The girls were well married; their father could count in case of need on the daggers and rifles of his sons-in-law. The son was only ten years old, but he was already showing signs of promise.

One autumn day Mateo and his wife set out early to visit one of his flocks in a clearing on the *maquis*. Little Fortunato wanted to go with them, but the clearing was too far off; besides, it was necessary for someone to stay and mind the house; so his father refused. We shall soon see that he had occasion to regret having done so.

He had been gone a few hours, and little Fortunato was quietly lying out in the sunshine, looking at the blue mountains, and thinking that on the following Sunday he would be going to town to have dinner with his uncle, the corporal,[1] when his meditations were suddenly interrupted by the firing of a gun. He got up and turned towards that part of the plain from which the sound had come. Other shots followed, fired at irregular intervals and coming nearer all the time. Finally, on the path which led from the plain to Mateo's house, a man appeared. He wore a pointed cap like a mountaineer, he was bearded and clothed in rags, and he was dragging himself along with difficulty, leaning on his gun. He had just been shot in the thigh.

This man was a *bandit*[2] who, having set out at night to get some powder from the town, had fallen on the way into an ambush of Corsican *voltigeurs*.[3] After a vigorous defence, he had succeeded in escaping, but they were hot in pursuit,

---

[1] Corporals were formerly the leaders the Corsican communes chose when they rebelled against the feudal lords. Today the name is still given some-times to a man who, by his property, his connexions, and his clients, exercises influence and a kind of effective magistracy over a *pieve* or canton. By ancient custom Corsicans are divided into five castes: *gentlemen* (of whom some are *magnifiques*, the others *signori*), *corporals, citizens, plebeians,* and *foreigners*.

[2] This word is used here to denote an outlaw.

[3] A body of soldiers raised in recent years by the Government, which acts in conjunction with the gendarmes in the maintenance of order.

D

firing at him from rock to rock. He had only a short start on the soldiers, and his wound made it out of the question for him to reach the *maquis* before being overtaken.

He came up to Fortunato and said:

'Are you the son of Mateo Falcone?'

'Yes.'

'I am Gianetto Sanpiero. I am being pursued by the yellow collars.[4] Hide me, for I cannot go any farther.'

'But what will my father say if I hide you without his permission?'

'He will say that you did right.'

'How do you know?'

'Hide me quickly: they are coming.'

'Wait till my father returns.'

'Good God, how can I wait? They will be here in five minutes. Come, hide me, or I will kill you.'

Fortunato replied with the utmost coolness:

'Your gun is unloaded, and there are no more cartridges in your *carchera*.'[5]

'I have my stiletto.'

'But can you run as fast as I can?'

With a bound he put himself out of reach.

'You are no son of Mateo Falcone! Will you let me be taken in front of your house?'

The child seemed moved.

'What will you give me if I hide you?' he said, drawing nearer.

The bandit felt in a leather pouch which hung from his belt and took out a five-franc piece, which he had probably put aside for powder. Fortunato smiled at the sight of the piece of silver and, seizing hold of it, he said to Gianetto:

'Don't be afraid.'

He quickly made a large hole in a haycock which stood next to the house. Gianetto crouched down in it, and the child covered him up so as to leave a little breathing space,

---

[4] The uniform of the *voltigeurs* was a brown coat with a yellow collar.

[5] A leather belt which served as both a cartridge-box and a wallet.

and yet in such a way as to make it impossible for anyone to suspect that the hay concealed a man. He went on to devise a rather ingenious stratagem worthy of a savage. He fetched a cat and her kittens and put them on top of the haycock to give the impression that it had not been touched for some time. Then, noticing some bloodstains on the path near the house, he carefully covered them with dust, and, this done, he lay down again in the sun with the utmost sang-froid.

A few minutes later six men wearing brown uniforms with yellow collars and under the command of a sergeant-major, stood before Mateo's door. This sergeant-major was a distant relative of the Falcones. (It is well known that further degrees of relationship are recognized in Corsica than anywhere else.) His name was Tiodoro Gamba; he was an energetic man, greatly feared by the bandits, several of whom he had already hunted down.

'Good day, cousin', he said, coming up to Fortunato. 'How you've grown! Did you see a man pass just now?'

'Oh, I'm not yet as tall as you, cousin', the child replied, with a foolish look.

'You soon will be. But, tell me, haven't you seen a man pass by?'

'Have I seen a man pass by?'

'Yes, a man with a pointed black velvet cap and a waistcoat embroidered in red and yellow.'

'A man with a pointed cap and a waistcoat embroidered in red and yellow?'

'Yes; answer me quickly, and don't repeat my questions.'

'The priest passed our door this morning on his horse Piero. He asked me how Papa was, and I replied. . . .'

'You're making fun of me, you rascal. Tell me at once which way Gianetto went, for it's him we're after, and I'm certain he took this path.'

'How do you know that?'

'How do I know that? I know you've seen him.'

'How could I see anybody passing by when I was asleep?'

'You weren't asleep, you little rogue; the shots woke you up.'

'So you think your guns are as noisy as that, do you, cousin? My father's rifle makes a lot more noise.'

'The devil take you, you young scamp. I'm absolutely certain you've seen Gianetto. Perhaps you've even hidden him. Here, you fellows, go into the house, and see if our man's there. He could only walk with one foot, and he's got too much common sense, the villain, to have tried to reach the *maquis* limping. Besides, the bloodstains stop here.'

'And what will Papa say?' Fortunato asked, with a chuckle. 'What will he say when he finds out that his house has been searched in his absence?'

'You little good-for-nothing, do you know that I can easily make you change your tune?' cried Sergeant-Major Gamba, seizing him by the ear. 'Perhaps you'll decide to talk when you've had a thrashing with the flat of a sword.'

Fortunato kept on laughing derisively.

'My father is Mateo Falcone', he said meaningly.

'Do you know, you young scamp, that I can take you off to Corte or to Bastia? I'll put you in a dungeon on a bed of straw, with your feet in irons, and I'll have you guillotined if you don't tell me where Gianetto Sanpiero is.'

The child burst out laughing at this ridiculous threat.

'My father is Mateo Falcone', he repeated.

'Sergeant-Major, don't let us get on the wrong side of Mateo', one of the soldiers whispered.

Gamba was obviously embarrassed. He talked in a low voice with his soldiers, who had already been all over the house. This was not a lengthy operation, for a Corsican hut only consists of a single square room. The furniture comprises a table, benches, boxes, cooking utensils, and hunting gear. All this time little Fortunato stroked his cat, and seemed to be taking a mischievous pleasure in the confusion of his cousin and the soldiers.

One soldier came up to the haycock. He looked at the cat and idly stirred the hay with his bayonet, shrugging his shoulders as if he considered the precaution ridiculous. Nothing moved, and the child's face did not betray the slightest emotion.

The sergeant-major and his band were nonplussed; already they were looking glumly towards the plain, as if they were half-inclined to return the way they had come; but their chief, convinced that threats would produce no effect upon Falcone's son, thought that he would make one last effort by trying the effect of flattery and presents.

'Cousin,' he said, 'you're a wide-awake lad, I can see. You'll get on in life. But you're playing a dangerous game with me; and, if I wasn't afraid of upsetting my cousin Mateo, I'll be damned if I wouldn't carry you off with me.'

'Bah!'

'But, when my cousin returns, I'll tell him all about it, and he'll whip you till he draws blood for having told me lies.'

'How do you know that?'

'You'll see. But, look here, be a good lad and I'll give you something.'

'Let me give you a piece of advice, cousin, and that is that if you wait any longer, Gianetto will reach the *maquis*, and then it will take a cleverer fellow than you to catch him.'

The sergeant-major took a watch out of his pocket, a silver watch worth at least ten crowns. Seeing how little Fortunato's eyes sparkled as he looked at it, he held it out at the end of its steel chain.

'You rogue,' he said, 'you'd like to have a watch like this hanging from your collar, and to go walking up and down the streets of Porto-Vecchio as proud as a peacock; people would ask you the time, and you'd reply: "Look at my watch!"'

'When I'm grown up, my uncle the corporal will give me a watch.'

'Yes; but your uncle's son has one already—though not such a fine one as this. . . . But then, he is younger than you are.'

The boy sighed.

'Well, would you like this watch, cousin?'

Fortunato ogled the watch out of the corner of his eyes, just as a cat does when a whole chicken is offered to it. It dares not pounce on the bird, because it is afraid a joke is being played on it, and it turns its eyes away now and then, to avoid succumbing to the temptation; but it keeps on licking its lips and it seems to be saying to its master: 'What a cruel joke you are playing on me!'

Sergeant-Major Gamba, however, seemed genuinely willing to hand over the watch. Fortunato did not hold out his hand; but he said to him with a bitter smile:

'Why are you making fun of me?'

'I swear I'm not doing anything of the sort. Just tell me where Gianetto is, and this watch is yours.'

Fortunato smiled incredulously, and fixed his black eyes on those of the sergeant-major. He tried to see from them how much faith he could place in his words.

'May I lose my epaulettes', exclaimed the sergeant-major, 'if I don't give you the watch on that condition! I call my men to witness so that I cannot break my word.'

As he spoke, he held the watch nearer and nearer until it almost touched the child's pale cheeks. The boy's face plainly expressed the conflict going on in his mind between covetousness and the claims of hospitality. His bare breast heaved violently, and he seemed close to choking. All the time the watch dangled and swung around, and sometimes touched the tip of his nose. Finally, little by little, his right hand rose towards the watch, his fingertips touched it; and its whole weight rested on his hand, although the sergeant-major still held the end of the chain. . . . The watch face was blue. . . . The case was newly polished. . . . In the sunlight it looked as if it were on fire. . . . The temptation was too strong.

Fortunato raised his left hand too, and pointed with his thumb over his shoulder at the haycock against which he was leaning. The sergeant-major understood him immediately, and let go of the end of the chain. Fortunato felt himself the sole owner of the watch. He jumped up with the agility of a deer, and moved a dozen paces away from the haycock, which the soldiers promptly started to overturn.

It was not long before they saw the hay move, and a bleeding man came out, holding a dagger; when, however, he tried to draw himself up, his stiffening wound prevented him from standing. He fell down. The sergeant-major threw himself upon him and snatched away his dagger. He was promptly trussed up securely, in spite of his resistance.

Stretched out on the ground and tied up like a bundle of faggots, Gianetto turned his head towards Fortunato, who had drawn nearer.

'Son of . . . !' he said to him, more in contempt than in anger.

The boy threw Gianetto the silver piece which he had given him, conscious that he no longer deserved it; but the outlaw did not appear to take any notice of this action. He said in a cool voice to the sergeant-major:

'My dear Gamba, I cannot walk; you will have to carry me to the town.'

'You could run faster than a kid just now', his captor retorted brutally. 'But don't worry; I'm so pleased to have caught you that I would carry you for a league on my own back without feeling tired. All the same, my friend, we'll make a litter for you with some branches and your cloak. The farm at Crespoli will provide us with horses.'

'All right', said the prisoner; 'I trust you'll put a little straw on your litter to make it more comfortable for me.'

While the soldiers were busy, some making a rough stretcher out of chestnut boughs and the others dressing Gianetto's wound, Mateo Falcone and his wife suddenly appeared round a bend in a path leading from the *maquis*. The wife was bent under the weight of a huge sack of chestnuts, while her husband was strolling along carrying nothing but a gun in one hand, and a second gun slung over his shoulder, for it is considered undignified for a man to carry any other burden but his weapons.

When he saw the soldiers, Mateo's first thought was that they had come to arrest him. But he had no ground for this fear, for he had never had any trouble with the law. On the contrary, he enjoyed a good reputation. But he was a Corsican and a man of the mountains, and there are few mountain-bred Corsicans who, if they search their memories sufficiently, cannot discover some little peccadillo, a shot, or a dagger thrust, or some such trifle. Mateo's conscience was clearer than most, for it was a good ten years since he had pointed his gun at any man; yet at the same time he was cautious, and he got ready to put up a brave fight if it should prove necessary.

'Wife,' he said to Giuseppa, 'put down your sack, hold yourself in readiness.'

She obeyed immediately. He gave her the gun which was slung over his shoulder, as it might have hampered his movements. Cocking the one in his hand, he advanced slowly towards the house, keeping close to the trees which bordered the path, and ready, at the slightest sign of hostility, to throw himself behind the largest trunk, and to open fire from that cover. His wife walked close behind him, holding his spare gun and his cartridge pouch. It was the duty of a good housewife, in the event of a fight, to reload her husband's firearms.

On his side, the sergeant-major was very uneasy at the sight of Mateo advancing like that upon them with measured steps, his gun pointed and his finger on the trigger.

'If by any chance Gianetto is related to Mateo,' he thought, 'or if he is a friend of his, and he means to protect him, two of his bullets will be put into two of us as sure as a letter goes to the post, and if he aims at me, in spite of our relationship . . .'

In this dilemma, he took a bold decision, which was to go forward alone towards Mateo to tell him what had happened, greeting him like an old acquaintance. But the short distance which separated him from Mateo seemed to him terribly long.

'Hullo, my old comrade', he called out. 'How are you, old fellow? It's your cousin Gamba.'

Mateo had stopped, without saying a word; and while the other was speaking, he gently raised the muzzle of his rifle so that by the time the sergeant-major reached him it was pointing skywards.

'Good day, brother.'[6]

'I just dropped in as I was passing to say good day to you and Cousin Pepa. We've done a long tramp today; but you've no need to feel sorry for us, for we've made a fine catch. We've captured Gianetto Sanpiero.'

'Thank goodness!' exclaimed Giuseppa. 'He stole one of our milch goats last week.'

Gamba rejoiced at these words.

'Poor devil!' said Mateo. 'He was hungry.'

'The fellow fought like a lion', continued the sergeant-major, slightly nettled. 'He killed one of my men, and, not content with that, he broke Corporal Chardon's arm; but that is not of great consequence, for the dead man was only a Frenchman. . . . Then he hid himself so cleverly that the devil couldn't have found him. If it hadn't been for my cousin Fortunato, I should never have discovered him.'

'Fortunato?' cried Mateo.

'Fortunato?' repeated Giuseppa.

'Yes; Gianetto had hidden under that haycock over there, but my cousin showed me his trick. I'll tell his uncle the corporal, who will send him a fine present as a reward. And both his name and yours will be in the report which I shall send to the Advocate General.'

'Damnation!' said Mateo under his breath.

By this time they had rejoined the soldiers. Gianetto had already been laid on his litter, and was ready to be taken away. When he saw Mateo in Gamba's company he smiled

---

[6] *Buon giorno, fratello*, the customary greeting of Corsicans.

a strange smile; then, turning towards the door of the house, he spat on the threshold, saying:

'This is a traitor's house!'

Only a man determined to die would have dared to utter the word 'traitor' in connexion with Falcone. A quick thrust with a dagger, which would not have needed to be repeated, would have immediately wiped out the insult. But Mateo made no other movement beyond putting his hand to his forehead like a man stricken with grief.

Fortunato had gone into the house when he had seen his father arrive. He soon reappeared carrying a jug of milk, which he offered with downcast eyes to Gianetto.

'Keep away from me!' roared the outlaw.

Then, turning to one of the soldiers, he said:

'Comrade, give me a drink of water.'

The soldier placed his flask in his hands, and the bandit drank the water given him by a man with whom he had only recently exchanged shots. He then asked that his hands might be tied crossed over his breast instead of behind his back.

'I like', he said, 'to lie comfortably.'

They granted him his request. Then the sergeant-major gave the signal for departure, said farewell to Mateo, who made no answer, and set off at a quick pace towards the plain.

Nearly ten minutes went by before Mateo opened his mouth. The child looked uneasily first at his mother, then at his father, who leant on his gun, looking at him with an expression of concentrated anger.

'Well, you have made a fine beginning', said Mateo at last in a voice which was calm, but terrifying to anyone who knew the man.

'Father!' the boy cried out, with tears in his eyes, going forward as if to throw himself at his knees.

'Out of my sight!' shouted Mateo.

The child stopped motionless a few paces from his father and began to sob.

Giuseppa came over to him. She had just seen the end of the watch-chain hanging outside his shirt.

'Who gave you that watch?' she asked sternly.

'My cousin the sergeant-major.'

Falcone seized the watch, and threw it against a stone with such force that it broke into a thousand pieces.

'Woman,' he said, 'is this my child?'

Giuseppa's brown cheeks turned brick-red.

'What are you saying, Mateo? Do you know to whom you are speaking?'

'All I know is that this child is the first member of his family to commit an act of treachery.'

Fortunato's sobs and hiccoughs redoubled, and Falcone kept his lynx eyes steadily fixed on him. Finally he struck the ground with the butt of his gun, flung it across his shoulder, and retraced his steps in the direction of the *maquis*, ordering Fortunato to follow him. The child obeyed.

Giuseppa ran after Mateo and seized him by the arm.

'He is your son', she said in a trembling voice, fixing her black eyes on her husband's as if in order to read what he was thinking.

'Let go', replied Mateo; 'I am his father.'

Giuseppa embraced her son, and went back crying into the hut. She threw herself on her knees in front of an image of the Virgin, and prayed fervently. In the meantime Falcone had walked about two hundred yards along the path before going down into a little ravine. He tested the ground with the butt of his gun, and found it soft and easy to dig. The spot struck him as suitable for his purpose.

'Fortunato, go over to that big rock.'

The boy did as he was told, then knelt down.

'Say your prayers.'

'Father, father, don't kill me!'

'Say your prayers!' repeated Mateo in a terrible voice.

The child recited the Lord's Prayer and the Creed, stammering and sobbing. The father said 'Amen!' in a loud voice at the end of each prayer.

'Are those all the prayers you know?'

'I know the *Ave Maria* and the litany my aunt taught me, father.'

'It's rather long, but never mind.'

The child finished the litany in a faint voice.

'Have you finished?'

'Oh, father, have mercy on me! Forgive me! I will never do it again. I will beg my cousin the corporal to pardon Gianetto.'

He went on talking. Mateo cocked his rifle and took aim.

'May God forgive you!' he said.

The boy made a frantic effort to get up and clasp his father's knees, but he had no time. Mateo fired, and Fortunato fell stone dead.

Without throwing a single glance at the body, Mateo set off on the way back to his house to fetch a spade with which to bury his son. He had only taken a few steps when he met Giuseppa, who had come running up, alarmed by the sound of the shot.

'What have you done?' she cried.

'Justice!'

'Where is he?'

'In the ravine. I am going to bury him. He died like a Christian. I shall have a Mass sung for him. Send word to my son-in-law Tiodoro Bianchi to come and live with us.'

1829

The Vision of Charles XI

'There are more things in heav'n and earth, Horatio,
Than are dreamt of in your philosophy.'

SHAKESPEARE: *Hamlet*

ALTHOUGH people laugh at visions and supernatural apparitions, several have been so well authenticated that if one refused to believe in them, one would have to reject the whole of historical testimony, lock, stock, and barrel.

A correctly drawn-up report, signed by four reliable witnesses, is the guarantee of the truth of the incident about to be related. I should add that the prediction set out in this report was known and cited a very long time before events which occurred in our days seemed to fulfil it.

Charles XI, father of the famous Charles XII, was one of the most despotic monarchs, but at the same time one of the wisest, who have reigned over Sweden. He restricted the monstrous privileges of the nobility, abolished the power of the Senate, and created laws by his own authority; in short, he changed the constitution of the country, which had previously been an oligarchy, and compelled the States to vest absolute control in him. He was, moreover, an enlightened man, steadfastly attached to the Lutheran religion, brave, cold, and matter-of-fact in character, and entirely devoid of imagination.

He had just lost his wife, Ulrica Eleanor. Although it is said that his severity had hastened her end, he held her in high regard, and seemed more affected by her death than would have been expected of a man so unfeeling. After that event he grew even more taciturn and gloomy than before, and gave himself up to work with an application which showed an urgent desire to dispel painful thoughts.

At the close of one autumn evening he was sitting in his

private apartment in the Stockholm Palace, in his dressing-gown and slippers, in front of a great fire. With him was his chamberlain, Count Brahé, who was one of his favourite courtiers, and the physician Baumgarten, who, it may be remarked in passing, set up for a sceptic, and wanted people to doubt everything except medicine. That evening the King had sent for him to advise on some slight ailment or other.

The evening wore on, but contrary to his habit the King made no sign of dismissal to his companions. He sat in deep silence, his head bowed, and his eyes fixed upon the burning embers, weary of their company, but afraid, without knowing why, of being left alone. Count Brahé had noticed that his presence was distasteful to the King, and had several times hinted that he feared His Majesty was in need of rest; but the King had indicated with a gesture that he wished him to remain. The physician, in his turn, spoke of the ill-effects to health of keeping late hours; but Charles replied between his teeth:

'Stay where you are; I don't feel like sleeping yet.'

The courtiers then tried several different topics of conversation, but all fell flat at the end of the second or third sentence. It seemed clear that His Majesty was in one of his black moods, and in such circumstances, the position of a courtier is extremely delicate. Count Brahé, suspecting that the King was brooding over the loss of his wife, gazed for some time at the portrait of the Queen which hung on the wall of the the room, and then exclaimed with a deep sigh:

'What an excellent likeness! That is exactly the expression the Queen wore, so majestic and yet so gentle.'

'Bah!' retorted the King, who always suspected an underlying reproach whenever anyone mentioned the Queen in his presence. 'That portrait is too flattering. The Queen was ugly.'

Then, inwardly vexed at his harshness, he rose and paced round the room to hide an emotion of which he was

ashamed. He stopped in front of the window which looked
on to the courtyard. It was a dark night and the moon was
in its first quarter.

The palace in which the kings of Sweden now reside was
not then finished, so that Charles XI, who had begun it,
lived in the old palace on the headland of the Ritterholm
overlooking Lake Malar. It was a vast building in the form
of a horseshoe. The King's private apartment was at one
end of the palace, and nearly opposite it was the large hall
where the States assembled to receive communications from
the Crown.

The windows of this hall appeared at this moment to be
illuminated with a bright light. This struck the King as
strange, but at first he thought the light might be produced
by the torch of some valet. Still, what could anybody be
doing there at such an hour, in a room which had not been
opened for a long time? Besides, the light was too bright to
come from a single torch. It could have been put down to a
fire, but there was no smoke, the windows were not broken,
and no sound could be heard; everything suggested simply
an illumination.

Charles watched the windows for some time in silence.
Meanwhile Count Brahé stretched out his hand towards
the bellrope to summon a page in order to send him to find
out the cause of this strange light, but the King stopped
him.

'I will go to the hall myself', he said.

While he spoke they saw his face grow pale, and his
expression revealed a sort of superstitious fear; but he went
out with a firm tread, followed by the chamberlain and
physician, each holding a lighted candle.

The porter, who had charge of the keys, was already in
bed. Baumgarten went to rouse him with an order from the
King to open immediately the doors of the assembly hall.
The man was greatly surprised at this unexpected order; he
dressed quickly, and joined the King with his bunch of
keys. First of all he opened the door of the gallery which was

used as an antechamber or private entrance to the assembly hall. The King went in and was astonished to find the walls completely draped in black.

'Who gave the order for draping this room in black?' he asked angrily.

'No one, Sire, to my knowledge', replied the startled porter. 'The last time I swept out the gallery it was panelled, as it always has been. . . . Certainly these hangings never came out of your Majesty's depository.'

The King, striding along at a rapid pace, had already walked more than two-thirds of the length of the gallery. The Count and porter followed close behind; the physician Baumgarten hung back a little, torn between the fear of being left alone and that of being exposed to the consequences of an adventure which had begun so strangely.

'Go no farther, Sire', exclaimed the porter. 'Upon my soul, there is some sorcery behind this. At this hour . . . since the death of the Queen, your gracious wife . . . they say she walks in this gallery. . . . May God protect us!'

'Stop, Sire', cried the Count in his turn. 'Do you not hear that noise coming from the assembly hall? Who knows to what dangers Your Majesty may be exposed?'

'Sire,' said Baumgarten, whose candle had just been blown out by a gust of wind, 'at least allow me to go and fetch a score of your halberdiers.'

'Let us go in', said the King sternly, stopping before the door of the great hall. 'Porter, open this door immediately.'

He kicked it, and the noise, echoing from the roof, resounded along the gallery like a cannon shot.

The porter trembled so much that his key rattled against the lock without his being able to find the keyhole.

'An old soldier trembling!' said Charles, shrugging his shoulders. 'Come, Count, you open this door for us.'

'Sire,' replied the Count, taking a step back, 'if Your Majesty commanded me to walk up to the mouth of a German or a Danish cannon I would obey unhesitatingly, but you wish me to defy the powers of hell.'

The King snatched the key from the hands of the porter.

'I see', he observed contemptuously, 'that I must attend to this matter myself.' And before his suite could prevent him he had opened the heavy oak door and entered the great hall, pronouncing the words 'With the help of God!' His three acolytes, urged by a curiosity stronger than fear, and perhaps ashamed to desert their King, went in after him.

The great hall was lit up by innumerable torches, and the old tapestries had been replaced by black hangings. Along the walls hung, as usual, German, Danish, and Russian flags—trophies taken by the soldiers of Gustavus Adolphus. In their midst were some Swedish banners, covered with mourning bands.

An immense assembly filled the benches. The four orders of the State were seated in their proper order. All were dressed in black, and this multitude of human faces, which seemed luminous against a dark background, so dazzled the eyes of the four witnesses of this extraordinary scene that not one of them could recognize a face he knew in the crowd. Thus an actor who stands before a large audience sees only a confused mass of faces, in which he is unable to distinguish a single individual.

Seated on the raised throne from which the King usually addressed the assembly, they saw a bleeding corpse wearing the royal insignia. At his right stood a child with the crown on his head and a sceptre in his hand; at his left an old man, or rather another spectre, leant against the throne. He was wearing the ceremonial cloak used by the former administrators of Sweden before Vasa had made it a Kingdom. In front of the throne, seated at a table covered with large books and a few parchments, were several grave and austere-looking personages, who looked like judges and were dressed in long black robes. Between the throne and the benches of the

E

assembly there was a block covered with black crape, and an axe lay near by.

No one in that supernatural assembly seemed to notice the presence of Charles and the three people with him. At their entry they could only hear at first a confused murmur of inarticulate words; then the oldest of the black-robed judges, the one who seemed to be president, rose and struck the book which lay open in front of him three times with his hand. A profound silence immediately fell. Then, through a door opposite the one which Charles had just opened, there came into the hall a few young men of noble bearing and richly dressed. Their hands were tied behind their backs, but they walked with heads erect and a confident air. Behind them a stalwart man in a jerkin of brown leather held the ends of the cords which bound their hands. The man who was walking in front, and who seemed to be the most important of the prisoners, stopped in the middle of the hall before the block and looked at it with proud disdain. While this was going on the corpse seemed to shake convulsively, and a stream of fresh crimson blood flowed from its wound. The youth knelt down and laid his head on the block; the axe flashed through the air and thudded down. A stream of blood gushed over the dais and mingled with that from the corpse; the head bounded several times on the reddened pavement, and then rolled as far as Charles's feet, which it dyed with blood.

Up to this moment surprise had held the King dumb, but this horrible sight unloosed his tongue. He took a few steps towards the dais, and, addressing himself to the figure wearing the Administrator's robes, he boldly uttered the well-known form of words:

'If thou art of God, speak; if thou art from the Other, leave us in peace.'

The phantom replied slowly in solemn tones:

'King Charles, this blood will not be shed during your reign . . .' (here the voice grew less distinct) 'but five reigns later. Woe, woe, woe to the House of Vasa!'

Then the spectres of the countless personages who formed this astonishing assembly gradually became fainter, until they soon looked like coloured shadows, and soon they disappeared completely. All the ghostly torches went out, and those of Charles and his suite now revealed only the old tapestries, stirring gently in the draught. They still heard for some time afterwards a melodious sound, which one of the witnesses compared to the murmur of the wind in the leaves, and another to the sound made by the strings of a harp when they break while the instrument is being tuned. All agreed to the duration of the apparition, which they judged to have lasted about ten minutes.

The black draperies, the severed head, the streams of blood which had stained the dais—all had vanished with the phantoms; only Charles's slipper retained a bloodstain, which in itself would have been sufficient to remind him of the scenes of that night, if they had not been all too deeply engraved in his memory.

When the King returned to his private apartment he had an account written of what he had seen, signed it himself, and had it signed by his fellow witnesses. In spite of the precautions taken to keep the contents of this document secret, it was soon known, even during the lifetime of Charles XI. It still exists, and up to the present time no one has thought fit to throw doubts upon its authenticity. In it the King concludes with these remarkable words:

'And if what I have just recounted is not the absolute truth, I renounce all hope of a better life to come, which I may have merited for a few good deeds, and above all for my zeal in working for the welfare of my people, and in preserving the faith of my forefathers.'

Now, if the reader recalls the death of Gustavus III, and the condemnation of Ankarstroem, his assassin, he will find several links between these events and the circumstances of this extraordinary prophecy.

The young man beheaded in the presence of the States was Ankarstroem.

The crowned corpse was Gustavus III.

The child was his son and successor, Gustavus Adolphus IV.

Finally, the old man was the Duke of Sudermania, uncle of Gustavus IV, who was regent of the realm, and in the end King, after the deposition of his nephew.

1829

The Storming of the Redoubt

A MILITARY friend of mine, who died of fever in Greece a few years ago, told me one day the story of the first engagement in which he had taken part. His account was so striking that I wrote it down from memory as soon as I had an opportunity. Here it is.

On the evening of 4 September I rejoined my regiment. I found the colonel in the bivouac. At first he received me rather coolly, but, after reading General B——'s letter of recommendation, his manner changed, and he said a few kind words to me.

He introduced me to my captain, who had just returned from a reconnoitring expedition. This captain, whose acquaintance I had scarcely time to make, was a tall, dark man, with a hard, forbidding expression. He had been a common soldier, and had won his commission and his cross on the battlefield. His voice was weak and hoarse, and contrasted strangely with his almost gigantic stature. I was told that this strange voice was due to a bullet which had gone right through him at the Battle of Jena.

On hearing that I came from the academy at Fontainebleau, he grimaced and said: 'My lieutenant died yesterday.' I understood that he meant to imply: 'You are supposed to take his place, and you aren't up to it.' A cutting reply rose to my lips, but I restrained myself.

The moon, coming up behind the Cheverino redoubt, which was situated about two gunshots from our bivouac, was large and red as it usually is when rising. But that evening it seemed to me to be unusually big. For a moment the redoubt was silhouetted against the shining orb, which looked like the cone of an erupting volcano. An old soldier, who was standing near me, remarked on the moon's colour.

'How red it is!' he said. 'That's a sign that it's going to cost us dear to take that precious redoubt.'

I have always been superstitious, and this omen, above all at such a moment, impressed me greatly. I lay down, but could not sleep. I got up and walked about for some time, looking at the long line of fires along the heights beyond the village of Cheverino.

When I thought that the fresh, sharp night air had sufficiently quickened my blood, I returned to the fire. I wrapped myself carefully in my cloak and closed my eyes, hoping not to open them again before the morning. But sleep stubbornly evaded me. Gradually my thoughts took on a melancholy character. I told myself that I had not a single friend among the hundred thousand men who covered that plain. If I were wounded I should go into hospital, there to be treated without consideration by ignorant surgeons. Everything I had heard about surgical operations returned to my memory. My heart started pounding, and instinctively I arranged my handkerchief and wallet over my chest as a kind of breastplate. I was overcome with weariness, and I became drowsier with every moment that passed, but at every moment some sinister thought occurred to me with greater force and woke me with a start.

Nevertheless, weariness finally won the day, and when the reveille sounded, I was fast asleep. We fell into rank; the roll was called; then we piled arms again, and everything suggested that we were going to pass a quiet day.

About three o'clock an aide-de-camp arrived, carrying a dispatch, and we were ordered to shoulder arms. Our skirmishers spread out over the plain; we followed them slowly, and in about twenty minutes' time we saw all the Russian outposts fall back and withdraw into the redoubt.

One artillery battery was set up on our right, another on our left, but both were well in front of us. They opened a sharp fire on the enemy, who answered briskly; and soon the Cheverino redoubt was hidden under thick clouds of smoke.

Our regiment was almost protected from the Russian fire by a ridge of earth. Their cannon-balls, which in any case rarely came our way, for they were aiming rather at our artillery, passed over our heads, or at the most showered us with earth and small stones.

The moment the order to advance was given, my captain looked at me so closely that I felt obliged to stroke my budding moustache two or three times with as nonchalant an air as possible. In fact, I was not at all frightened, and my only fear was that people might think me afraid. Furthermore, those harmless cannon-balls contributed to preserve my heroic composure. My vanity told me that I was really in danger, since I was at last under fire from a battery. I was delighted to find myself so cool, and I thought of the pleasure of telling the story of the taking of the Cheverino redoubt in Madame de B——'s Rue de Provence drawing-room.

The colonel rode past our company and said to me: 'Well, you're going to have a rough time of it in your first engagement.'

I smiled with a truly military air, at the same time brushing from my sleeve some dust that a cannon-ball, which had fallen thirty paces away, had thrown up.

It seems that the Russians must have noticed the ill success of their cannon-balls, for they replaced them with shells which could more easily reach us in the hollow where we were posted. A fairly big explosion knocked off my cap and killed a man close to me.

'I congratulate you', the captain said to me, after I had picked up my cap. 'Now you are safe for the day.'

I was familiar with that military superstition that the axiom *non bis in idem* holds good as much on the battlefield as in the court of justice. I jauntily put my cap on again.

'That's a rather free and easy greeting', I said as jovially as possible. This poor joke seemed excellent in the circumstances.

'You are lucky', said the captain; 'nothing else will happen to you, and you will be in command of a company tonight,

for I know that I shan't see tomorrow. Every time I have
been wounded the officer next to me has been hit by a spent
bullet, and', he added in a lower tone and almost as if he
were ashamed, 'their names always began with a P.'

I pretended not to be superstitious; most people would
have done the same; most people would have been equally
struck by such prophetic words. Conscript as I was, I knew
that I could not confide my feelings to anybody, and that I
must always appear cool and brave.

Half an hour later, the Russian fire slackened considerably, and we sallied out of our corner to storm the redoubt.

Our regiment was composed of three battalions. The
second was ordered to outflank the redoubt from the side
of the gorge; the other two were to make the assault. I was
in the third battalion.

Coming out from behind the sort of breastwork which
had protected us, we were greeted by several rounds of fire,
which did only a little harm in our ranks. The whistling of
the balls startled me: I kept looking round, thus bringing
upon myself a few jocular remarks from my more seasoned
comrades.

'All considered,' I said to myself, 'a battle isn't as bad as
all that.'

We advanced at the double, preceded by our sharp-
shooters; suddenly the Russians gave three cheers, three
distinct hurrahs, then stopped firing and fell silent.

'I don't like that silence', said my captain; 'it bodes no
good to us.'

I thought our men were a little too noisy, and I could not
help inwardly contrasting their tumultuous clamour with
the impressive silence of the enemy.

We quickly came to the foot of the redoubt, where the
palisades had been broken and the earth thrown up by our
cannon-balls. The soldiers leapt upon these fresh ruins with
shouts of '*Vive l'Empereur!*' which were louder than one
would have expected from men who had already shouted so
much.

I raised my eyes, and I shall never forget the sight I beheld. Most of the smoke had lifted and was hanging like a canopy about twenty feet above the redoubt. Through a blue haze I could see the Russian grenadiers, with arms fixed, as motionless as statues, behind their half-destroyed parapet. I can see now each soldier, his left eye fixed on us, his right hidden by his raised gun. In an embrasure a few feet from us, a man holding a lighted fuse was standing by a cannon.

I shuddered, and I thought my last hour had come.

'Now the fun's going to begin', cried my captain. 'Here goes!'

Those were the last words I heard him speak.

A roll of drums sounded in the redoubt. I saw all the muskets levelled. I closed my eyes, and heard an appalling din, followed by shrieks and groans. I opened my eyes, surprised to find myself still alive. The redoubt was once again wrapped in smoke. I was surrounded by wounded men and corpses. My captain lay stretched out at my feet; his head had been smashed by a cannon-ball, and I was covered with his brains and blood. Out of the whole of my company there were only six men and myself left standing.

A moment of stupor followed this carnage. The colonel, putting his hat on the end of his sword, was the first to climb the parapet, shouting: '*Vive l'Empereur!*' He was promptly followed by all the survivors. No longer have I any clear recollection of what followed. Somehow or other we entered the redoubt. We fought hand to hand in such dense smoke that we could not see each other. I suppose I had a hit, for I found my sword covered with blood. At last I heard the shout of 'Victory!' and, as the smoke cleared away, I saw the ground of the redoubt covered with blood and corpses. The guns especially were buried under piles of corpses. Scattered about in disorder stood about two hundred men in French uniform, some loading their guns, others wiping their bayonets. Eleven Russian prisoners were with them.

The colonel was lying covered with blood on a broken

powder-chest near the gorge. A few soldiers were tending him; I went over.

'Where is the senior captain?' he was asking a sergeant.

The sergeant shrugged his shoulders in a significant way.

'And the senior lieutenant?'

'Here is the gentleman who arrived yesterday', said the sergeant in a perfectly calm voice.

The colonel smiled bitterly.

'Well, Monsieur, you are in command', he said to me. 'Have the gorge of the redoubt fortified at once with these wagons, for the enemy is in force; but General C—— will send you reinforcements.'

'Colonel,' I said to him, 'are you badly wounded?'

'Done for, my dear fellow. But we've taken the redoubt!'

Tamango

CAPTAIN LEDOUX was a born sailor. He had started as an ordinary seaman and worked his way up to the rank of assistant helmsman. At the Battle of Trafalgar, his left hand was smashed by a splinter of wood and had to be amputated; afterwards he received his discharge, together with first-rate testimonials. The monotony of a quiet life was distasteful to him, and, when the chance of going to sea again presented itself, he signed on as a second lieutenant on a privateer. The money which came to him as his share of a few captures enabled him to buy books and to study the theory of navigation, a science of which he already had a thorough practical knowledge. In due time he became captain of a pirate lugger with three guns and a crew of sixty, and the longshoremen of Jersey still remember the exploits of this pirate ship. Then came the peace, which was a great grief to him; he had amassed a small fortune during the war and had been hoping to increase it at the expense of the English. But he was obliged to offer his services to peaceful merchants; and, as he was known to be a man of experience and determination, he had no difficulty in finding a ship. When slave-trading was prohibited by law, and to undertake it, it was necessary not only to evade the watchfulness of the French Customs officers, which was not so very difficult, but also to escape being captured by English cruisers, Captain Ledoux proved invaluable to these ebony merchants.[1]

Unlike most sailors who, like him, have spent a long time in subordinate positions, Captain Ledoux had not that deep-rooted dread of innovation, nor that addiction to routine, which they all too often retain when they have been promoted. On the contrary, he was the first to suggest to his

[1] The name the slave-traders gave themselves.

ship-builder the use of metal tanks for holding fresh water. He also had the handcuffs and the chains with which all slave-ships were equipped made in a particular fashion and carefully varnished to prevent their rusting. But what redounded most to his credit with all the slave-traders was the brig he had constructed under his personal supervision and according to his own ideas. He had christened her *Hope.* Built for slave-trading, she was a fast sailing-ship, narrow and long like a warship, and yet able to hold a vast number of blacks. He had the 'tween-decks made narrow and low— only forty inches high in fact, maintaining that that left sufficient room for any slave of reasonable stature to sit at ease—and why should they want to stand up? There would be more than enough standing for them when they reached the colonies, he used to say.

The Negroes would sit with their backs against the sides of the ship in two parallel lines, leaving a free space between their feet which, in all other slave-ships, was only used as a gangway. It was Ledoux's idea to make use of this free space by putting more Negroes there, forcing them to sit at right angles to the others. In this way his brig held at least ten more Negroes than any other ship of the same size. At a pinch, even more could have been put on board, but he was humane enough to allow each Negro a space measuring about five feet by two in which to stretch his limbs during the journey of six weeks or more. For after all, niggers were human beings like white men, he explained to his shipwright, as an excuse for this generous allowance of space.

The *Hope* weighed anchor in the port of Nantes on a Friday—a fact which superstitious people subsequently recalled. The Customs officers who carefully searched the brig did not come across six large cases full of chains, handcuffs, and those irons which for some unknown reason were called the 'bonds of justice'. Nor did they express any surprise at the huge supply of fresh water which the *Hope* was carrying, in spite of the fact that according to her papers she was only going to Senegal for the purpose of trading in wood and ivory. Admittedly the voyage was not a long one, but there was no harm in erring on the safe side—for if they happened to be becalmed, what would become of them without water?

So the *Hope* set sail on a Friday, well provisioned and well equipped. Ledoux would perhaps have liked the masts to be a little stronger, but as long as he was in command of the ship he had no reason to complain of them. He had a speedy, easy voyage to the African coast. The anchor was lowered in the River Joal, I believe, that portion of the coast being at the time unguarded by English cruisers; and the native merchants immediately came on board.

The moment could not have been more favourable. Tamango, a well-known warrior and slave-dealer, had just reached the coast with a large convoy of slaves which he was selling cheap with the confidence of a man who feels that he has the power of meeting any demands as soon as the article of his trade becomes scarce.

Captain Ledoux went ashore and called on Tamango. He found him in a straw hut which had been hastily erected for him, together with his two wives and a few subordinate traders and slave-drivers. Tamango had dressed up to receive the white captain. The old blue uniform which he wore could still be recognized as having been a corporal's, but there were two gold epaulettes on each shoulder, both fastened to the same button and hanging down, one in front, the other behind. As he was not wearing a shirt, and the tunic was too short for a man of his size, a large band of black skin, which looked like a broad belt, was visible between the white facings of the uniform and his canvas breeches. A heavy cavalry sword which hung at his side was fastened by a string, and he was holding a fine double-barrelled rifle of English make. Thus equipped, the African warrior doubtless considered himself more than a match for the most exquisite dandy from London or Paris.

Captain Ledoux stared at him for some time in silence, and Tamango, enjoying the impression which he thought he

was making on the white man, drew himself up like a
grenadier being inspected by a foreign general. Ledoux,
after examining him with the eye of a connoisseur, turned
to his chief officer and observed:

'There's a strapping fellow who would fetch at least a
thousand crowns if we could only land him safe and sound
in Martinique.'

They sat down and the customary greetings were exchanged, a sailor who had a smattering of the Volof language acting as interpreter. A cabin-boy brought along a
basket full of bottles of brandy, drinking began at once, and
the captain, in order to put Tamango in a good humour, made
him a present of a fine copper powder-flask with a portrait
of Napoleon embossed on it. The gift was acknowledged with
a due show of gratitude. The company then left the hut and
sat outside in the shade, in front of the bottles of brandy,
and Tamango gave the signal for the slaves he had to sell to
be brought along.

They came forward in a long file, their bodies bent by
fear and fatigue, all bearing on their shoulders a fork over
six feet long, the two prongs of which were fastened at the
back of the neck with a wooden bar. Whenever they set out,
one of the slave-drivers shoulders the handle of the yoke of
the first slave, who picks up that of the man behind him;
the second slave carries the yoke-handle of the third slave,
and so on with the others. When a halt is called, the leader
of the file drives the pointed end of his yoke-handle into
the ground and the whole column comes to a standstill.
Naturally, there can be no question of escape from the file
with a heavy yoke six feet long fastened round one's
neck.

The captain shrugged his shoulders as each slave, male or
female, passed before him; he found the men puny, the
women too old or too young, and complained of the
degeneracy of the black race.

'Everything is deteriorating', he declared. 'It was very
different in the old days when every woman was five feet

six, and four men could easily have worked a frigate's capstan and raised the sheet anchor.'

However, while making these criticisms he picked out a first assortment of blacks, choosing the strongest and the best looking, for whom he was willing to pay the usual price; on the remainder he demanded a considerable reduction. Tamango, for his part, defended his interests; he cried up his wares, and spoke of the scarcity of men and the dangers of the traffic. He ended by quoting a price—I do not know what—for the slaves the white captain wanted to take on board.

Ledoux stared at him in amazement and indignation when the interpreter had translated Tamango's proposal into French. Then he got up, muttering frightful oaths, apparently with the intention of putting an end there and then to all bargaining with a man so unreasonable. But Tamango restrained him and with some difficulty persuaded him to sit down again. Another bottle was opened and the discussion renewed. Now it was the black man's turn to call the white man's proposals outrageous and extravagant. They shouted and argued and drank prodigious quantities of brandy; but the brandy had very different effects on the two contracting parties. The more the Frenchman drank the less he offered, and the more the African drank the less he insisted on his demands. So, when the last bottle was empty, it was found that they had come to terms. In exchange for one hundred and sixty slaves, Tanamgo accepted some cheap cotton goods, powder, and gun-flints, three casks of brandy, and fifty rusty rifles. The captain, to ratify the compact, shook the half-tipsy Negro by the hand, and immediately the slaves were handed over to the French sailors, who lost no time in putting iron chains and handcuffs on them in place of their wooden yokes—a striking demonstration of the superiority of European civilization.

There were still about thirty slaves—children, old men, or infirm women—left. But there was no more room on board. Tamango, not knowing what to do with these left-overs, offered to sell them to the captain at the rate of a bottle of brandy a head. The offer was a tempting one. Ledoux remembered a performance of *The Sicilian Vespers* at Nantes, at which he had seen a considerable number of big, stout people enter the pit, which was already full, and none the less manage to sit down thanks to the compressibility of human bodies. He agreed to take the twenty slimmest of the thirty slaves.

Tamango then offered to dispose of the remaining ten for a glass of brandy a head. Ledoux reflected that children go half-price and take up half-room in public vehicles. So he accepted three children, but said that he would not take even one more black. Tamango, seeing himself left still with seven slaves on his hands, seized his rifle and took aim at the nearest woman. She was the mother of the three children.

'Buy her,' he said to the white man, 'or I'll kill her. Half a glass of brandy, or I fire.'

'But what the devil am I to do with her?' asked Ledoux.

Tamango fired, and the slave fell dead.

'Now for another!' cried Tamango, taking aim at a decrepit old man. 'A glass of brandy, or else . . .'

The bullet went off at random, for one of his wives had knocked his arm. She had just recognized in the old man whom her husband was about to kill a *guiriot*, or magician, who had prophesied that she would be queen.

Tamango, maddened by the brandy he had drunk, lost control of himself at finding himself thwarted. He hit his wife savagely with the butt of his gun, and turned towards the captain.

'Take her', he said. 'I'll make you a present of this woman.'

She was pretty. Ledoux looked at her with a smile and took her by the hand.

'I'll manage to find room for her', he said.

The interpreter, a humane man, asked Tamango for the remaining six slaves in exchange for a cardboard snuff-box. He took off their yokes and told them to go where they liked.

They promptly hurried away in different directions, at a loss to know how to reach their homes, two hundred leagues from the coast.

In the meantime the captain took his leave of Tamango and set to work getting his cargo on board. It was not safe to remain any longer in the river, as the cruisers might return at any moment, so he made up his mind to set sail the next day. As for Tamango, he lay down on the grass in the shade, to sleep off the effects of the brandy.

When he woke up the vessel was already under sail and moving down the river. Tamango, still fuddled from the effects of his recent debauch, called for his wife Ayché. He was reminded that she had been unfortunate enough to incur his displeasure, and that he had made a present of her to the white captain, who had taken her on board with him. Dumbfounded at this news, Tamango slapped his forehead; then he took his gun and, knowing that the river made several detours before it reached the sea, he ran by the most direct route towards a little creek about a mile from the sea. There he hoped to find a canoe in which to overtake the brig, delayed in her voyage as she would be by the winding river. He was not mistaken; sure enough, he had time to jump into a boat and catch up with the slave-ship.

Ledoux was surprised to see him, and even more so to learn that he wanted his wife back.

'Once given, a present cannot be returned', he replied. And he turned his back on him.

The black insisted, offering to give back some of the goods he had received in exchange for the slaves. The captain laughed, and told him that Ayché was a fine woman and that he intended to keep her. The unfortunate Tamango burst into a torrent of tears, and groaned and uttered cries of anguish as shrill as those of a man undergoing a surgical operation. He rolled about the deck calling for his beloved Ayché, and dashed his head against the planks as if he were trying to commit suicide. The captain, quite unmoved, pointed to the shore, indicating that it was time for him to

F

go. But Tamango persisted, even going to the length of offering his golden epaulettes, his sword, his rifle. It was all in vain.

Meanwhile the lieutenant of the *Hope* said to the captain: 'Three slaves died on us last night: why not take this lusty rascal in their place? He's worth the three of them put together.'

Ledoux reflected that Tamango was indeed worth at least a thousand crowns, that this voyage, which promised to be exceptionally remunerative, would probably be his last, and finally, that since his fortune was made and he was giving up the slave trade, it didn't matter what sort of a reputation he left behind on the coast of Guinea. Besides, there was not a soul in sight on the shore, and the black chieftain was entirely at his mercy. It would only be a matter of disarming him, for it would hardly be safe to lay hands on him while he still had arms in his possession. So Ledoux asked him for his gun, as if he wished to examine it to see whether it was really worth exchanging for the beautiful Ayché. While he was scrutinizing it, he took care to jerk the charge out. The lieutenant for his part was handling the sword, so that Tamango was unarmed. Two sturdy sailors sprang on him. But the black put up a heroic struggle as soon as he recovered from his surprise, and fought for a long time with the two sailors in spite of the disadvantage at which they had him. Thanks to his tremendous strength he managed to get to his feet, and with one blow he felled the man who was holding him by the collar. Leaving a piece of his coat in the hands of the other sailor, he hurled himself like a madman upon the lieutenant, to regain his sword, and received a cut on the head which, without going deep, made a large wound. He fell a second time, and the sailors promptly bound him hand and foot. While he was defending himself, he yelled with rage and struggled like a wild boar caught in a net; but when he saw that all resistance was useless, he shut his eyes and remained absolutely motionless. Only his heavy and hurried breathing showed that he was still alive.

'By heaven,' exclaimed the captain, 'won't the blacks he sold us laugh when they see him a slave like them! They'll all begin to think there must be such a thing as Providence.'

Meanwhile poor Tamango was losing a great deal of blood. The charitable interpreter, who, the day before, had saved the lives of six slaves, came to bind up his wound and speak a few words of comfort to him. No record exists of what he said, and the Negro remained as motionless as a corpse. Two sailors had to carry him like a package down to his allotted place in the 'tween-decks. For two days he refused to have anything to eat or drink and he scarcely opened his eyes. His companions in captivity, once his prisoners, had seen him appear in their midst with uncomprehending amazement. So great was the fear which he still inspired in them, that not one of them dared to jeer at the misery of the man who was the cause of their own.

Favoured by a strong land breeze, the vessel was soon out of sight of the coast of Africa. The captain's mind, already at ease with regard to the English cruiser, was now occupied exclusively with the huge profits waiting for him in the colonies towards which he was sailing. His cargo of ebony was keeping well. There were no contagious diseases. Only twelve Negroes had died of suffocation, and they were among the weakest—a mere trifle. In order to preserve his human cargo as much as possible from the ill effects of the voyage he had them brought up on deck once a day. Three successive batches of these unhappy slaves came up to inhale, for one hour each time, the stock of fresh air which was to last through the twenty-four hours. A portion of the crew mounted guard over them, armed to the teeth for fear of insurrection; they also took care that the slaves were never entirely freed from their shackles. Sometimes a sailor who could play the violin would treat them to some music, and it was strange to see them all turn their black faces towards the fiddler, gradually lose their look of abject despair, burst into loud laughter, and clap their hands too, when their chains would allow them. Exercise being essential to health, one of Captain Ledoux's salutary practices was to make the slaves dance frequently, just as horses are made to prance when embarked on a long voyage.

'Come along, my beauties, dance and amuse yourselves!' the captain would shout in a voice of thunder, cracking a heavy horsewhip. And in less than no time the poor blacks would be leaping and dancing.

For some time Tamango's wound kept him below the hatches. But at length he appeared on deck; at first he stood in the midst of the crowd of cringing slaves, holding his head high, and gazing sadly but calmly over the vast expanse of water which surrounded the ship; then he lay down, or rather slumped on the deck, without even troubling to arrange his chains in a less awkward position. Ledoux was sitting behind him on the quarter-deck, quietly smoking his pipe. Near him stood Ayché, holding in her hand a tray of liqueurs which she was ready to pour out for him. She was unfettered, and was wearing a pretty blue cotton dress and dainty morocco shoes. It was obvious that she occupied a place of honour in the captain's domestic circle. One of the blacks who loathed Tamango motioned to him to look in that direction. Tamango turned his head, caught sight of her, cried out, and springing up impetuously, ran towards the quarter-deck before the sailors on guard could prevent such a flagrant breach of naval discipline.

'Ayché!' he shouted at the top of his voice—and Ayché gave a cry of terror—'do you think that there is no Mama Jumbo in the land of the white man?'

Sailors were already running up with raised clubs, but he folded his arms and walked calmly back to his place, as if unmoved, while Ayché burst into a flood of tears, apparently petrified by these mysterious words.

The interpreter explained what this awful Mama Jumbo was, whose very name aroused such terror.

'It is the Negroes' bogy-man', he said. 'When a husband is afraid his wife is going to behave as many wives do, in

France as well as in Africa, he threatens her with Mama Jumbo. I have seen Mama Jumbo with my own eyes, and I saw how the trick was worked; but the poor blacks ... they are so simple; they don't understand anything. Picture to yourself a group of women dancing one evening—having a *folgar*, as they call it in their dialect—near a thick, dark grove. Suddenly some weird music was heard, but nobody could be seen making it, for all the musicians were hidden in the trees. There were reed flutes, wooden drums, *balafos*, and guitars made of half a gourd, all playing a tune calculated to frighten the devil himself. No sooner did the women hear the tune than they began to tremble and would have run away if their husbands had not prevented them; they knew perfectly well what was going to happen. Suddenly a huge white figure as tall as our topgallant-mast came out of the wood, with a head as big as a bushel, eyes like hawse-holes, and a mouth like the devil's, full of fire. It was walking slowly, very slowly, and it did not come more than half a cable's length away from the grove. The women cried: "It's Mama Jumbo", shrieking like fishwives. And their husbands said to them: "Come on, you bitches, tell us if you've behaved yourselves; if you lie, Mama Jumbo is there to gobble you up alive." Some of the women were foolish enough to admit everything, and then their husbands proceeded to give them a sound thrashing.'

'But what was that white figure, that Mama Jumbo?' asked the Captain.

'Why it was only some joker dressed up in a white sheet, holding up on the end of a stick a hollow pumpkin, with a lighted candle inside, which served as a head. It was nothing worse than that, for it doesn't require much ingenuity to fool a nigger. But, when all's said and done, it's not such a bad idea, that Mama Jumbo of theirs; and I wish my wife believed in it.'

'If my wife isn't afraid of Mama Jumbo,' said Ledoux, 'she is frightened of Master Stick, and she knows well enough how I'd treat her if she played any pranks with me.

We aren't a long-suffering family, we Ledoux, and even though I've only one hand left it can still use a rope's-end to some purpose. As to that joker who started the subject of Mama Jumbo, tell him to behave himself and not to frighten this little woman again, or I'll have him flogged till his black skin turns as red as an underdone beefsteak.'

With these words the captain went down to his cabin, sent for Ayché, and tried to comfort her; but neither his caresses nor his blows (for there was a limit to the captain's patience) succeeded in pacifying the beautiful Negress; her tears flowed in torrents. The captain went up on deck in a bad temper and vented his feelings on the officer on duty concerning the course he was steering just then.

During the night, when nearly all the crew were sound asleep, the men on watch heard first a low, sad, solemn chant, which seemed to come from the 'tween-decks, and then the piercing shriek of a woman. Immediately afterwards, Ledoux's fierce voice, swearing and threatening, and the sound of his heavy whip echoed through the whole vessel. A moment later, silence fell once more. The next day, Tamango came on deck with his face bruised, but still looking as proud and determined as ever.

As soon as Ayché saw him she rushed from the quarterdeck, where she had been sitting beside the captain, ran to Tamango, and fell on her knees before him, exclaiming in a frenzy of despair:

'Forgive me, Tamango, forgive me!'

Tamango looked at her steadily for a minute, and seeing that the interpreter was out of earshot, he said:

'A file!'

Then, turning his back on her, he lay down on the deck. The captain reproved her sharply, even struck her once or twice, and forbade her ever again to speak to her ex-husband. But he had not the slightest inkling of the meaning of the few words they had exchanged, and he did not ask any questions about them.

Meanwhile Tamango, locked up with the other slaves,

exhorted them night and day to make a great effort to regain their liberty. He spoke to them of the small number of the white men, and drew their attention to the increasing carelessness of their guards; then, without going into details, he assured them that he would find some way of leading them back to their country, boasted of his knowledge of occult sciences, which the Negroes hold in great respect, and declared that any who refused to assist in the attempt would incur the wrath of the devil. All these harangues were delivered in the dialect of the Peuls, which was known to most of the slaves, but which the interpreter did not understand. The orator's reputation, and the slaves' habit of fearing and obeying him, aided his eloquence wonderfully, and the blacks begged him to fix a day for their emancipation long before he considered that he was in a position to carry it out. He told the conspirators vaguely that the time had not yet come, and that the devil, who appeared to him in his dreams, had not yet given the word; but that they should hold themselves in readiness for the first signal. In the meantime he lost no opportunity of testing the vigilance of his guards. One day he saw a sailor who had left his rifle leaning against the gunwale, watching a shoal of flying-fish which were following the ship. Tamango took the rifle and began to handle it, imitating the grotesque gestures, the movements which he had seen performed by sailors at drill. The rifle was taken from him after a few moments, but he had learnt that it was possible to touch a weapon without at once arousing suspicion. When the time came for him to use one in earnest, woe betide the man who tried then to snatch it from his hands!

One day Ayché threw him a biscuit, making at the same time a sign which he alone understood. The biscuit contained a small file, and on that tool hung the success of the plot. At first Tamango took care not to let his companions see the file; but, when night had fallen, he began to murmur unintelligible words, accompanied by weird gestures. Gradually he became more and more excited, and the murmurs increased to cries. As they listened to the varied intonations of his voice, the slaves felt convinced that he was engaged in an animated conversation with an unseen person. They all started trembling, not doubting that the devil was at that very moment in their midst. Tamango brought this scene to an end by exclaiming joyfully:

'Comrades, the spirit which I have conjured up has at last fulfilled his promises, and I hold in my hand the instrument of our deliverance. Now you only need to summon up a little courage, and you will be free.'

Those near him were allowed to feel the file, and the trick, gross as it was, took in these even grosser men.

At last, after many days of waiting, the great day of liberty and vengeance dawned. The conspirators, sworn to secrecy by a solemn oath, had laid their plans after careful deliberation. When it was the turn of the most determined slaves, including Tamango, to go on deck, they were to seize the arms of their guards; a few others were to go to the captain's cabin to fetch the rifles which were kept there. Those who had succeeded in filing through their fetters were to lead the attack; but in spite of several nights' persistent toil, the majority of the slaves were still unable to take an energetic part in the action. So three lusty Negroes were detailed to kill the man who carried the keys to the fetters in his pocket, and to go at once to set their companions free.

That day Captain Ledoux seemed in the best of tempers. Contrary to his usual habit, he pardoned a cabin-boy who had incurred a flogging. He congratulated the officer of the watch on his seamanship, told the crew he was pleased with their work, and promised to give them all a gratuity at Martinique, which they would reach very soon. All the sailors promptly began to amuse themselves by planning how they were going to use the gratuity. They were thinking about brandy and the coloured women of Martinique when Tamango and his fellow conspirators were brought up on deck.

They had been careful to file their fetters in such a way that they did not appear to be cut, but at the same time so that the slightest movement would be enough to break them. Moreover, they rattled their chains so much that anybody hearing them would have thought that they were twice as heavily laden as usual. After sniffing the air for some time, they all joined hands and began to dance, while Tamango intoned his tribal war song[2] which he always used before going into battle. After they had danced for a while, Tamango, as if tired out, stretched himself at full length at the feet of a sailor who was leaning nonchalantly against the ship's bulwarks; all the other conspirators followed his example, so that each of the guards was surrounded by several blacks.

Suddenly Tamango, who had just quietly broken his fetters, gave a tremendous shout, which was to serve as a signal, seized the sailor near him violently by the legs, threw him head over heels, and, planting his foot on his stomach, wrenched his gun away from him and shot the officer of the watch. Simultaneously, every other sailor on duty was attacked, disarmed, and his throat promptly cut.

On all sides a war-cry was raised. The boatswain's mate, who had the keys to the fetters, was one of the first victims. In a moment the deck was swarming with a horde of blacks. Those who could not find arms seized the bars of the capstan or the oars of the longboat. From that moment the European crew was doomed; a few sailors made a show of resistance on the quarter-deck, but they lacked weapons and resolution. Ledoux, however, was still alive, and had lost none of his courage. Seeing that Tamango was the soul of the conspiracy, he hoped that if he could kill him he might be able to make short work of his accomplices. So he ran off in search of him, sword in hand, calling to him at the top of his voice. Tamango promptly rushed at him, holding his gun by the barrel and using it as a club. The two leaders met in one of the gangways, the narrow passage leading aft from

[2] Each Negro chief has his own.

the quarter-deck. Tamango was the first to strike. By a slight movement of his body the white man avoided the blow: the butt end of the musket, falling violently on the planks, was smashed, and the weapon was dashed out of Tamango's hand. He stood defenceless, and Ledoux, with a diabolical grin, raised his arm and prepared to run him through. But Tamango, as agile as the panthers of his native country, sprang into his adversary's arms and seized the hand in which he was holding his sword. The one strained to hold his weapon, the other to wrench it away. During this desperate struggle both men fell, but the African was underneath. Without losing heart, Tamango hugged his adversary with all his strength, and bit his neck so savagely that the blood spurted out as if under a lion's teeth. The sword slipped from the captain's nerveless hand. Tamango seized it, sprang up, and, his mouth streaming with blood, gave a yell of triumph as he stabbed his dying enemy through and through.

Victory was no longer in doubt. The few remaining sailors begged the Negroes to have pity on them, but all, even the interpreter who had never done them any harm, were mercilessly massacred. The lieutenant died heroically. He had withdrawn aft, beside one of those small cannons which turn on a pivot and are loaded with grape-shot. With his left hand he worked the gun and with his right wielded a sword to such good effect that he attracted a crowd of Negroes round him. Then he fired the gun into this dense mass and blasted a wide path paved with dead and dying. The next moment he was torn to pieces.

When the body of the last white man had been hacked to pieces and thrown overboard, the Negroes, their thirst for vengeance satiated, looked up at the ship's sails, which were swollen by the fresh breeze and seemed to be still obeying their oppressors and taking the victors, in spite of their triumph, towards the land of slavery.

'So nothing has been achieved!' they thought sadly. 'Will

this great fetish of the white men take us back to our country now that we have shed the blood of its masters?'

Some of them said that Tamango would be able to make the fetish obey, so they started shouting for him.

He was in no hurry to appear. They found him standing in the fore cabin, one hand resting on the captain's bloody sword, the other stretched out to his wife Ayché, who was on her knees before him kissing it. But the joy of victory could not diminish a sombre anxiety which was visible in every line of his face. Less obtuse than the rest, he was better able to understand the difficulties of the situation.

At last he came up on deck, affecting a serenity which he did not feel. Urged by a hundred confused voices to change the course of the vessel, he advanced towards the helm with slow steps, as if to postpone for a while the moment which would determine both for himself and for the others the extent of his power.

Not even the most stupid Negro on board had failed to notice the influence exercised on the movements of the ship by a certain wheel and the box fixed in front of it, but the whole mechanism was a profound mystery to them. Tamango examined the compass for a long time, moving his lips as if he were reading the characters which he could see printed on it; then he put his hand to his forehead and assumed the pensive attitude of a man doing mental arithmetic. All the Negroes stood round him, their mouths agape, their eyes wide open, anxiously following his slightest movement. At last, with that mixture of fear and confidence which ignorance inspires, he gave the wheel a tremendous turn.

Like a noble steed which rears when some imprudent rider drives in his spurs, the good ship *Hope* bounded over the waves at this incredible manœuvre, as if in her indignation she wished to sink together with her stupid pilot. The necessary link between the direction of the sails and that of the helm being suddenly broken, the ship heeled over so violently that it looked as if she were going to founder. Her long yards plunged into the sea; several men were thrown off their balance and some fell overboard. Soon the ship righted herself and stood proudly against the swell, as if to fight once again against destruction. But the wind increased its efforts and suddenly, with a deafening crash, the two masts fell, snapped off a few feet above the deck, which was covered with wreckage and a tangled network of ropes.

The terrified Negroes fled below decks, howling with fear, but as there was nothing left to catch the breeze, the vessel righted herself and allowed herself to be rocked gently by the waves. Then the more daring of the blacks came up again and began clearing away the debris littering the deck. Tamango remained motionless, leaning on the binnacle, his face buried in his folded arm. Ayché was beside him, but did not dare to speak to him. Gradually the Negroes approached him; a murmur arose, which soon turned into a torrent of insults and abuse.

'Traitor! Impostor!' they cried. 'You are the cause of all our misfortunes: it was you who sold us to the white men, and it was you who forced us to rebel against them. You boasted of your wisdom, and promised to take us back to our homes. We believed you, fools that we were, and just now we were all nearly killed because you offended the white man's fetish.'

Tamango raised his head proudly and the Negroes standing round him fell back in alarm. He picked up two guns, beckoned to his wife to follow him, and made for the bows of the vessel. There he constructed a sort of barricade of planks and empty barrels; then he sat down behind this entrenchment from which the bayonets of his two muskets projected menacingly. The others left him alone.

Some of the Negroes were in tears, while others raised their hands to the sky, and called on their own and the white man's fetishes; some, kneeling before the compass and marvelling at its ceaseless movements, implored it to take them back to their country, and yet others lay on the decks

in a state of abject despair. Among these wretches were
women and children screaming with terror, and a score of
wounded men begging for help which no one thought of
giving them.

All of a sudden a Negro appeared on deck, his face beam-
ing with joy. He announced that he had just discovered the
place where the white men stored their brandy; his excite-
ment and his expression clearly showed that he had already
sampled it. This piece of news silenced for a while the cries
of the unfortunate blacks. They rushed down to the store-
room and gorged themselves with liquor. An hour later
they were all dancing and laughing on deck, abandoning
themselves to all the excesses of brutish drunkenness. Their
singing and dancing were accompanied by the groans and
sobs of the wounded. The rest of the day and the whole
night were spent in this fashion.

Next morning, when they awoke, despair again possessed
them. During the night a great number of the wounded had
died. The vessel was surrounded by floating corpses, and
clouds were lowering over a heavy sea. They held a conference. A few apprentices in the art of magic, who had not
dared to speak of their skill in front of Tamango, now
offered their services in turn, and several potent incantations
were tried. The failure of each attempt increased the general
despondency until at last someone suggested appealing to
Tamango, who was still behind his barricade. After all, he
was the wisest of them all, and he alone could extricate
them from the desperate plight into which he had brought
them. An old man approached him with overtures of peace,
and begged him to come and give them his advice. But
Tamango, as inexorable as Coriolanus, turned a deaf ear to
his pleas. During the night, in the midst of the tumult, he
had laid in a supply of biscuits and salt meat. He appeared
to have no intention of leaving the solitude of his retreat.

There was still plenty of brandy left. That, at all events,
helped them to forget the sea, slavery, and the approach of
death. They slept, and in their dreams they saw Africa with

its forests of gum trees, its thatched huts, and its baobabs, whose foliage shaded whole villages. The orgy of the day before was renewed, and continued for several days. They did nothing but howl and weep and tear their hair, and then get drunk and sleep. Several died of drink, and a few jumped into the sea or stabbed themselves.

One morning Tamango left his stronghold and went up to the stump of the mainmast.

'Slaves,' he said, 'the Spirit has appeared to me in a dream and revealed to me the means of taking you back to your country. You deserve to be abandoned to your fate as punishment for your ingratitude, but I pity these women and these wailing children. I forgive you. Listen!'

All the Negroes bowed their heads respectfully, and gathered round him.

'Only the white men', continued Tamango, 'know the mystic words which move these huge wooden houses; but we can steer without difficulty those small boats which are like our own.'

He pointed to the sloop and the other ship's boats.

'Let us fill them with provisions, get into them, and row in the direction of the wind. My Master and yours will make it blow towards our country.'

They believed him. No plan could have been more reckless. Not knowing how to use the compass, and ignorant as to their whereabouts, they could not do anything but row at random. Tamango's belief was that by rowing straight ahead he was certain to come, sooner or later, to a land inhabited by black men; for he had heard his mother say that the white men lived in their ships, and that the black men possessed the earth.

Soon everything was ready to be embarked, but only the sloop and one dinghy were found to be serviceable. It was impossible to find room for the eighty or so Negroes who were still alive, so the sick and wounded had to be abandoned. Most of them begged to be killed rather than be left behind.

After endless difficulties the two boats were got under way, so overloaded that the choppy sea threatened to swamp them at any moment. Tamango and Ayché were in the sloop, which, being clumsier and more heavily laden, was soon left far behind by the dinghy. The wailing of a few poor wretches who had been left behind on board the brig was still audible when a big wave suddenly caught the sloop athwart and swamped her. In less than a minute she had disappeared. The blacks in the dinghy saw the catastrophe, and started rowing twice as hard, for fear of having to pick up a few survivors. Nearly all who were in the sloop were drowned. Only a dozen or so managed to get back to the brig; among them were Tamango and Ayché. When the sun set they could see the dinghy disappearing over the horizon; no one knows what became of it.

Why should I weary the reader with a revolting description of the tortures of hunger? About a score of human beings, crowded together in a narrow space, now tossed about on a stormy sea, now scorched by the burning sun, fought daily over the scanty remains of their provisions. Every piece of biscuit was the object of a fight, and the weaker died, not because the stronger killed him, but because he let him expire. After a few days only two people were still alive on board the good ship *Hope*—Ayché and Tamango.

One night there was a rough sea and a high wind, and it was so dark that one end of the ship could not be seen from the other. Ayché was lying on a mattress in the captain's cabin and Tamango was sitting at her feet. They had not spoken a word for hours.

'Tamango,' exclaimed Ayché at last, 'it is I who have brought all this suffering upon you.'

'I am not suffering', he answered brusquely, and threw the half-biscuit which he still had left on to the mattress beside her.

'Keep it for yourself', she said, gently pushing the biscuit away. 'I am no longer hungry. Besides, why eat? Has not my hour come?'

Tamango got up without answering and staggered up to the deck, where he sat down at the foot of one of the broken masts. With his head lolling on his breast, he began to whistle his tribal song. Suddenly he heard a loud cry above the noise of the wind and the sea; a light appeared; other shouts followed, and a huge black ship glided swiftly past the brig—so close that her yards passed over Tamango's head. He only saw two faces in the light of a lantern which hung from a mast. These men shouted again; then their ship, swept along by the wind, disappeared into the darkness. No doubt the men on watch had caught sight of the disabled ship, but the heavy weather prevented them from changing course. The next moment Tamango saw the flash of a cannon and heard the report; then he saw another flash, but heard no report; then he saw nothing more. The next day, there was not a sail to be seen on the horizon. Tamango lay down on his mattress again and closed his eyes. His wife Ayché had died that night.

I do not know how long it was before an English frigate, the *Bellona*, sighted a dismasted vessel, to all appearances abandoned by her crew. They sent a sloop alongside and found a dead Negress on her and a Negro so haggard and thin that he looked like a skeleton. He was unconscious, but there was still a breath of life left in him. The surgeon took charge of him and did what he could for him, so that by the time they reached Kingston, Tamango was in perfect health. He was asked to give an account of his adventures, and he told them everything he knew. The Jamaican planters wanted him to be hung as a rebellious black; but the governor, a kind-hearted man, took an interest in him, and found his actions justifiable since he had only acted in self-defence; besides, the men he had murdered were only Frenchmen. He was treated in the same way as the blacks who are found on board a captured slave-trader. They set him free, that is to say they made him work for the Government; but he was given threepence a day beside his keep.

One day the colonel of the 75th caught sight of this fine figure of a man and made him a drummer in his regimental band. Tamango learnt a little English, but hardly ever spoke. On the other hand, he was always drinking rum and tafia. He died in hospital of congestion of the lungs.

1829

The Etruscan Vase

AUGUSTE SAINT-CLAIR was not at all a favourite in what is called Society, the chief reason being that he only tried to please those who took his own fancy. He avoided some and sought the company of others. What is more, he was absent-minded and indolent. One evening, as he was coming out of the Théâtre-Italien, the Marquise A—— asked him how Mademoiselle Sontag had sung. 'Yes, Madame', Saint-Clair replied, smiling pleasantly and thinking of something totally different. This ridiculous reply could not be set down to shyness, for he talked to great lords and great men and even to society women with as much ease as if he had been talking to his equals. The Marquise decided that Saint-Clair was a stupid, impertinent boor.

One Monday he had an invitation to dine with Madame B——. She paid him a good deal of attention, and on leaving her house, he remarked that he had never met a more agreeable woman. Madame B—— spent a month collecting witticisms at other people's houses, which she dispensed in one evening at her own. Saint-Clair called upon her again on the Thursday of the same week. This time he was a little bored. Another visit decided him never to enter her drawing-room again. Madame B—— gave out that Saint-Clair was an ill-bred young man, with no manners at all.

He was naturally tender-hearted and affectionate, but, at an age when lasting impressions are acquired too easily, his demonstrative nature had drawn upon him the sarcasm of his comrades. He was proud and ambitious, and set store by the opinion of others, as children do. Henceforth he made a point of hiding any outward sign of what he considered a discreditable weakness. He attained his end, but his victory cost him dear. He learnt to hide the emotions of his tender heart from others, but repressing them only increased their force a hundredfold. In Society he won the sorry reputation of being heartless and indifferent; and, when alone, his anxious imagination plagued him with torments all the more hideous in that he could not reveal them to anyone.

How difficult it is to find a friend! Difficult? Is it possible? Have there ever been two men anywhere who have had no secrets from each other? That Saint-Clair had little faith in friendship was easy to see. With young Society people his manner was cold and reserved. He never asked any questions about their secrets; and most of his actions and all his thoughts were mysteries to them. Frenchmen love to talk about themselves; therefore Saint-Clair was the unwilling recipient of many confidences. His friends—a word denoting people we see about twice a week—complained of the lack of trust he showed in them; for indeed, he who confides his secrets to us unasked generally takes offence at not learning ours in return. People imagine that indiscretion should be reciprocal.

'He keeps his thoughts to himself', said the handsome Major Alphonse de Thémines one day; 'I could never place the least confidence in that devil Saint-Clair.'

'I think he's something of a Jesuit', replied Jules Lambert. 'Someone swore to me that he had met him twice coming out of Saint-Sulpice. Nobody knows what he thinks. I must say I never feel at ease with him.'

They separated. Alphonse met Saint-Clair on the Boulevard Italien, walking with his eyes on the ground, not noticing anyone. Alphonse stopped him, took his arm, and, before they had reached the Rue de la Paix, he had told to him the whole story of his love affair with Madame ——, whose husband was so jealous and so violent.

The same evening Jules Lambert lost all his money at cards. After that he started dancing. While dancing, he accidentally knocked against a man who had also lost all his money and was in a very bad temper. Sharp words followed and a challenge was given and taken. Jules begged Saint-

Clair to act as his second and, at the same time, borrowed some money from him, which he never remembered to repay.

All things considered, Saint-Clair was quite easy to get on with. He was no one's enemy but his own; he was obliging, often genial, rarely tiresome; he had travelled a great deal and read a great deal, but never spoke of his travels or his reading unasked. In personal appearance he was tall and well-built; he had a noble, refined expression, which was almost always too grave, but his smile was extremely attractive.

I am forgetting one important point. Saint-Clair paid attention to all women, and sought their company more than that of men. It was difficult to say whether he was in love; but if that cold creature was capable of love, then the beautiful Comtesse Mathilde de Coursy was the woman of his choice. She was a young widow, at whose house he was often seen. As proof of their intimacy there was the evidence first of the almost exaggerated politeness of Saint-Clair towards the Countess, and vice versa; then his habit of never pronouncing her name in public, or if obliged to speak of her, never with the slightest praise; also, before Saint-Clair was introduced to her, he had been passionately fond of music, and the Countess equally so of painting. Since they had become acquainted their tastes had changed. Lastly, when the Countess had gone to take the waters the previous year, Saint-Clair had left less than a week later.

My duty as an historian obliges me to reveal that early one morning in July, a few moments before sunrise, the garden gate of a country house opened, and a man crept out with the stealthiness of a burglar fearing discovery. This country house belonged to Madame de Coursy, and the man was Saint-Clair. A woman, wrapped in a cape, came to the gate with him and stood with her head out to watch him as long as she could, while he walked away along the path which led by the park wall. Saint-Clair stopped, looked round cautiously, and motioned with his hand for the woman to go in. The light of a summer dawn enabled him to distinguish her pale figure, standing motionless in the same place. He went back to her, and clasped her tenderly in his arms. He meant to compel her to go in, but he still had a hundred things to say to her. Their conversation had lasted ten minutes when they heard the voice of a peasant leaving his cottage to go to his work in the fields. One more kiss was exchanged, the gate was shut, and Saint-Clair in one bound reached the end of the footpath.

He followed a road which was obviously well known to him, and ran along, striking the bushes with his stick and almost jumping for joy. Sometimes he stopped, or walked along slowly, looking at the sky, which was turning crimson in the east. In short, anyone meeting him would have taken him for an escaped lunatic. After half an hour's walk he reached the door of a lonely little house which he had rented for the season. He let himself in with a key, and then, throwing himself on a couch, he fell into a daydream, with staring eyes and a gentle smile playing on his lips. His mind was filled with happy thoughts. 'How fortunate I am!' he kept repeating. 'At last I have met a heart that understands mine. . . . Yes, I have found my ideal. . . . I have gained at the same time a friend and a mistress. . . . What character! . . . What a passionate soul! . . . No, she has never loved anyone before me.' Soon, since vanity always enters into human affairs, he thought: 'She is the loveliest woman in Paris', and his imagination conjured up all her charms. 'She has chosen me before all the others. She had the flower of society at her feet. That colonel of hussars, handsome, brave, and not too fatuous; that young author who paints such pretty watercolours and is such a capital actor; that Russian Lovelace who has been in the Balkan campaign and served under Diébitch; above all, Camille T——, who has a clever wit, good manners, and a fine sabre cut across his forehead . . . she has dismissed them all in favour of me! . . .' Then came his refrain: 'Oh, how fortunate I am! How fortunate I am!'

He got up and opened the window, for he could scarcely breathe, next he walked up and down, and then he rolled about on his couch.

A happy lover is almost as much of a bore as an unhappy one. One of my friends, who was often in one or other of these conditions, found that the only way of getting any attention was to give me an excellent breakfast, during which he was free to talk of his amours. Once the coffee was finished he was obliged to change the subject.

As I cannot give breakfast to all my readers, I shall spare them Saint-Clair's ecstasies. Besides, it is impossible to live in cloud-cuckoo-land all the time. Saint-Clair was tired; he yawned, stretched his arms, saw that it was broad daylight, and finally decided to think about having some sleep. When he awoke he saw by his watch that he had barely time to dress and rush off to Paris, to attend a luncheon-party with several of his young friends.

Another bottle of champagne had just been uncorked. I leave my readers to guess how many had preceded it. It is sufficient to know that the company had reached that stage which comes quickly enough at a young men's luncheon-party, when everybody speaks at once, and when the steady heads begin to feel anxious about those who cannot carry so much.

'I wish,' said Alphonse de Thémines, who never missed a chance of talking about England, 'I wish that it was the custom in Paris, as it is in London, for every man to propose a toast to his mistress. If it were, we should find out for whom our friend Saint-Clair is pining.' And with these words he filled up his own glass and those of his neighbours.

Saint-Clair, a little embarrassed, was about to reply when Jules Lambert forestalled him.

'I heartily approve of that custom', he said, raising his glass; 'and hereby I adopt it. To all the milliners of Paris, with the exception of those over thirty, the one-eyed, and the lame.'

'Hurrah! Hurrah!' shouted the young anglomaniacs. Saint-Clair rose, glass in hand.

'Gentlemen,' he said, 'I have not such a large heart as our friend Jules, but it is more constant—a constancy all the more meritorious in that I have long been separated from the lady of my thoughts. Nevertheless I am sure that you will approve of my choice, if indeed you are not already my rivals. To Judith Pasta, gentlemen! May we soon welcome back the first *tragédienne* of Europe.'

Thémines was about to criticize the toast, but was interrupted by a chorus of cheers. Having parried this thrust, Saint-Clair believed himself safe for the rest of the day.

The conversation turned first on theatres. Theatrical censorship served as a transition to political topics. From the Duke of Wellington the talk passed to English horses, and from English horses to women, by a natural connexion of ideas; for, to young men, a good horse first, and then a beautiful mistress, are the two most desirable things in life.

Then the company discussed the means of acquiring these coveted treasures. Horses are bought, and some women can be bought too; but let us not talk of them. Saint-Clair, after modestly pleading inexperience with regard to this delicate subject, gave as his opinion that the chief way to attract a woman was to be singular, to be different from others. But he did not think it possible to give a general prescription for singularity.

'Then according to your view,' said Jules, 'a lame man or a hunchback would have a better chance with the ladies than a man with a straight back who looks like anybody else.'

'You push things too far,' retorted Saint-Clair, 'but I am willing to accept all the consequences of my proposition. For example, if I were a hunchback, instead of blowing my brains out, I would set out to make conquests. In the first place, I would try my wiles on only two sorts of women: either those who are really tender-hearted, or on those women—and there are a great many of them—who make themselves out to be original—eccentric, as they say in

England. To the former, I should describe my pitiful condition, and point out that I was the victim of Nature's cruelty. I should try to move them to sympathy with my lot, and I should let them suspect that I was capable of a passionate love. I should kill one of my rivals in a duel, and I should poison myself with a weak dose of laudanum. After a few months they would cease to notice my hump, and then it would be up to me to watch for the first signs of affection. As for the women who aspire to originality, their conquest is easy. Only persuade them that it is a hard and fast rule that a deformed person can never obtain a woman's favours, and they will immediately wish to prove the opposite.'

'What a Don Juan!' cried Jules.

'As we have the misfortune of not being hunchbacks,' said Colonel Beaujeu, 'we had better get our legs broken, gentlemen.'

'I fully agree with Saint Clair', said Hector Roquantin, who was only three and a half feet high. 'Every day the most beautiful and fashionable women give themselves to men whom you handsome fellows would never suspect.'

'Hector, get up and ring the bell for some more wine, will you?' said Thémines casually.

The dwarf got up and everyone smiled, recalling the fable of the fox which has its tail cut off.

'As for me,' said Thémines, resuming the conversation, 'the longer I live, the more clearly I see that the chief singularity which attracts even the most obdurate, is a passable face'—and he threw a complacent glance in the mirror opposite—'a passable face and good taste in dress.' And he flipped a crumb of bread off the lapel of his coat.

'Bah!' cried the dwarf. 'With a handsome face and a coat by Staub, there are plenty of women to be had for a week at a time, but one is tired of them at the second meeting. One needs more than that to win love, true love. . . . One needs . . .'

'Stop!' interrupted Thémines. 'Do you want a conclusive illustration? You all know Massigny, and you know what kind of man he was. Manners like an English groom, and no more conversation than his horse. ... But he was as handsome as Adonis, and could tie his cravat like Brummel. Altogether he was the greatest bore I have ever known.'

'He almost killed me with boredom', said Colonel Beaujeu. 'Just think, I once had to travel two hundred leagues with him!'

'Did you know', asked Saint-Clair, 'that he caused the death of poor Richard Thornton, whom you all knew?'

'But', objected Jules, 'I thought he was murdered by brigands near Fondi?'

'Granted; but, as you will see in a moment, Massigny was at all events an accomplice in the crime. A party of travellers, including Thornton, had arranged to go to Naples together to avoid being waylaid by brigands. Massigny asked to be allowed to join them. As soon as Thornton heard this, he set out before the others, apparently for fear of having to spend a few days with Massigny. He started alone, and you know the rest.'

'Thornton did right', said Thémines; 'he chose the easier of two deaths. We should all have done the same in his place.' Then, after a pause, he went on:

'Then you grant me that Massigny was the greatest bore on earth?'

'Certainly', they all cried with one accord.

'Don't let us deprive other candidates of all hope', said Jules; 'let us make an exception in favour of ——, especially when he is explaining his political plans.'

'Next you will grant me', continued Thémines, 'that Madame de Coursy is as clever a woman as can be found anywhere.'

A moment's silence followed. Saint-Clair bowed his head, imagining that all eyes were fixed on him.

'Who disputes it?' he said at last, still bending over his plate and apparently examining with great attention the flowers painted on the china.

'I maintain,' said Jules, raising his voice, 'I maintain that she is one of the three most delightful women in Paris.'

'I knew her husband', said the Colonel. 'He often showed me charming letters she had written to him.'

'Auguste,' interrupted Hector Roquantin, 'do introduce me to the Countess. They say you can do anything with her.'

'When she returns to Paris at the end of autumn', murmured Saint-Clair. 'I—I believe she does not entertain visitors in the country.'

'Will you listen to me?' exclaimed Thémines.

Silence was restored. Saint-Clair fidgeted on his chair like a prisoner in an Assize Court.

'You did not know the Countess three years ago because you were then in Germany, Saint-Clair', continued Alphonse de Thémines, with infuriating coolness. 'You cannot have any idea, therefore, what she was like at that time: beautiful, as fresh as a rose, vivacious above all else, and as gay as a butterfly. Well, do you know, among her many admirers, who was the one she honoured with her favours? Massigny! The most stupid and ridiculous of men turned the head of the most intelligent of women. Do you suppose that a hunchback could have done as much? Of course not! Believe me, with a handsome face and a good tailor, one can be sure of success.'

Saint-Clair was in a most difficult position. He longed to give the speaker the lie direct, but was restrained by the fear of compromising the Countess. He would have liked to say something in her favour, but he was tongue-tied. His lips trembled with rage, and he tried in vain to find some indirect means of forcing a quarrel.

'What!' exclaimed Jules in astonishment. 'Madame de Coursy gave herself to Massigny? Frailty, thy name is woman!'

'The reputation of a woman being of such small moment, it is, of course, permissible to tear it to shreds simply to raise a laugh', observed Saint-Clair in a dry, scornful voice; 'and . . .'

But as he spoke he remembered with dismay a certain Etruscan vase which he had noticed a hundred times on the mantelpiece in the Countess's house in Paris. He knew that it was a gift from Massigny, who had brought it back with him from Italy; and, worse still, it had been taken by the Countess from Paris to her country house. Every evening, when Mathilde took the flowers out of her dress, she put them in the Etruscan vase.

Speech died on his lips. He could neither see nor think of anything but that Etruscan vase.

'How absurd', some critic will object, 'to suspect his mistress on account of such a trifling detail!'

Have you ever been in love, my dear critic?

Thémines was in too good a humour to take offence at the tone Saint-Clair had used when speaking to him, and replied lightly and pleasantly:

'I can only repeat what people said. The story was generally accepted while you were in Germany. However, I scarcely know Madame de Coursy. It is eighteen months since I was last at her house. It may be that people were wrong, and the story was a fabrication of Massigny's. But let us return to our discussion, for whether my illustration be false or not does not affect my point. You all know that the cleverest woman in France, whose works . . .'

The door opened, and Théodore Néville came in. He had just returned from Egypt.

'Théodore, back so soon!' He was overwhelmed with questions.

'Have you brought back a real Turkish costume?' asked Thémines. 'Have you got an Arabian horse and an Egyptian groom?'

'What sort of man is the Pasha?' said Jules.

'When will he make himself independent? Have you seen a head cut off with a single stroke of the sword?'

'And the *almées*', said Roquantin. 'Are the women of Cairo beautiful?'

'Did you meet General L——?' asked Colonel Beaujeu.

'How has he organized the Pasha's army? Did Colonel C—— give you a sword for me?'

'And the Pyramids? The cataracts of the Nile? And the statue of Memnon? Ibrahim Pasha?' etc. They all talked at once; Saint-Clair thought of nothing but the Etruscan vase.

Théodore sat down with his legs crossed, for he had acquired that habit in Egypt and had been unable to shake it off in France. He waited till his questioners were tired, and then he spoke as follows, fast enough to save himself from being easily interrupted.

'The Pyramids! I assure you they are a regular fraud. They aren't half as high as I expected. Why, Strasbourg Cathedral is only twelve feet lower. I've had my fill of ancient monuments. Don't talk to me about them. The very sight of a hieroglyph would make me faint. There are plenty of travellers who take an interest in that sort of thing! My object was to study the nature and manners of that strange crowd which throngs the streets of Alexandria and Cairo—Turks, Bedouins, Copts, fellahin, and Moghrebins. I took a few hasty notes when I was in the lazaretto. What a foul place that is! I hope none of you fellows believes in infection! For my part, I smoked my pipe calmly in the midst of three hundred plague-stricken people. Oh, Colonel, you would admire the cavalry out there, and their splendid horses. I must show you some superb weapons I have brought back. I have a *djerid* which belonged to the famous Mourad Bey. I have a *yataghan* for you, Colonel, and a *khandjar* for Auguste. You must see my *metchla*, my *bournous*, and my *hhaïck*. Do you know I could have brought back some women with me if I had wanted to? Ibrahim Pasha has so many imported from Greece that they can be had for nothing. . . . But I had to think of my mother's feelings. . . . I talked a great deal with the Pasha. He is a thoroughly intelligent man, without any old-fashioned ideas. You would hardly credit how well he understands our affairs. Upon my honour, he knows the smallest secrets of our Cabinet. I gleaned some valuable

information from him on the state of the parties in France.
... Just now he is very interested in statistics. He subscribes
to all our papers. Would you believe it, he is an ardent
Bonapartist, and talks of nothing but Napoleon. "Oh, what
a great man *Bounabardo* was!" he said to me. "Bounabardo"
is how they pronounce Bonaparte.'

'*Giourdina*, meaning Jourdain', murmured Thémines.

'At first', continued Théodore, 'Mohammed Ali was
extremely reserved with me. All the Turks are very mistrustful, you know, and he took me for a spy or a Jesuit,
devil take me! He has a perfect horror of Jesuits. But, after
several visits, he recognized that I was an unprejudiced
traveller, anxious to inform myself fully about Eastern
customs, manners, and politics. Then he unbosomed himself
and spoke freely to me. At the third and last audience he
granted me, I ventured to say to him: "I don't understand
why Your Excellency doesn't make himself independent of
the Porte." "By Allah!" he replied, "I would like to, but
I fear the Liberal papers which manage everything in your
country would not support me if I proclaimed the independ-
ence of Egypt." He is a fine old man, with a splendid white
beard, who never laughs. He gave me some excellent preserves; but of all the presents I gave him, the one which
pleased him most was the collection of the costumes of the
Imperial Guard by Charlet.'

'Is the Pasha of a romantic turn of mind?' asked Thémines.

'He does not take much interest in literature; but you
know, of course, that Arabian literature is entirely romantic.
They have a poet called Melek Ayatalnefous-Ebn-Esraf,
who has recently published a book of *Meditations*, compared
with which Lamartine's read like classic prose. I hired a
teacher of Arabic as soon as I got to Cairo, with whom I
started reading the Koran. Although I did not have many
lessons, I had enough to be able to judge the sublime beauty
of the prophet's style, and of the mediocrity of all our trans-
lations. Look here, would you like to see some Arabian

script? This word in gold letters is *Allah,* which means
God.'

As he spoke he showed them an extremely grubby letter,
which he had taken out of a scented silk purse.

'How long did you stay in Egypt?' asked Thémines.

'Six weeks.'

And the traveller proceeded to hold forth on everything
from the cedar to the hyssop. Saint-Clair left almost immediately after his arrival, and went off in the direction of
his country house. The impetuous gallop of his horse
prevented him from following a consecutive train of thought,
but he felt vaguely that his happiness in this life had gone
for ever, and that it had been shattered by a dead man and
an Etruscan vase.

When he reached his house he threw himself on the same
couch on which he had analysed his happiness at such length
and so deliciously the day before. His most cherished idea
had been that his mistress was different from other women,
that she had not loved and could never love anyone but
himself. Now this beautiful dream had disappeared, in the
light of a sad and cruel reality. 'I have a beautiful mistress,
but that is all. She is an intelligent woman; she is therefore
all the more to be blamed for loving Massigny! . . . Admittedly she loves me now . . . with her whole soul . . . as
well as she can love. But to be loved in the same fashion as
Massigny was loved! . . . She yielded to my attentions, my
cajoleries, my importunities. But I was mistaken. There was
no affinity between our hearts. Whether her lover was
Massigny or myself was all one to her. He is handsome, and
she loves him for his good looks. I amuse her once or twice.
"I may as well love Saint-Clair", she said to herself, "since
the other is dead! And if Saint-Clair dies, or I tire of him, we
shall see what we shall see."

I firmly believe the devil listens invisible beside a wretch
who tortures himself like this. The enemy of mankind is
amused by the spectacle, and as soon as the victim's wounds
begin to heal, the devil is there to re-open them.

Saint-Clair thought he heard a voice murmur in his ears:

> The peculiar honour
> Of being the successor. . . .

He sat up on the couch and darted wild glances around him. How glad he would have been to find someone in his room! He would probably have torn him limb from limb.

The clock struck eight. At eight-thirty the Countess expected him. Should he disappoint her? Why, indeed, should he ever see Massigny's mistress again? He lay down again on his couch and shut his eyes. 'I will try to sleep', he said. He lay still for half a minute, then leapt to his feet and ran to the clock to see how the time was going. 'How I wish it were half past eight!' he thought. 'Then it would be too late for me to set off.' In his heart of hearts he had not the courage to stay at home without an excuse; he would have liked to be really ill. He walked up and down the room, then sat down and took a book; but he could not read a single syllable. He sat down at his piano, but had not the heart to open it. He whistled, looked at the clouds, and tried to count the poplars outside his windows. At last he consulted the clock again and saw that he had not succeeded in whiling away as many as three minutes. 'I cannot help loving her', he cried, grinding his teeth and stamping his foot; 'she rules me, and I am her slave, just as Massigny was before me. Well, poor wretch, since you haven't sufficient courage to break the hated chain, you must obey.' He picked up his hat and rushed out.

When we are carried away by a great passion it is some consolation to our self-esteem to look down from the height of our pride upon our weakness. 'It is true that I am weak', we say to ourselves; 'but if I chose not to be . . .'

As he walked slowly up the footpath which led to the garden gate, he could see in the distance a white figure standing out against the dark background of the trees. She was waving to him with her handkerchief. His heart beat violently, and his knees trembled; he could not speak, and

he had become so nervous that he was afraid the Countess
might read his ill-humour on his face.

He took the hand she held out to him, and kissed her
forehead, because she threw herself into his arms. He
followed her into the drawing-room in silence, scarcely able
to suppress sighs which seemed bound to burst his breast.

A single candle lighted the Countess's room. They sat
down, and Saint-Clair noticed his mistress's *coiffure*; a single
rose in her hair. He had given her, the previous evening, a
beautiful English engraving of Lesly's *Duchess of Portland*
(whose hair was dressed in the same fashion), and Saint-
Clair had merely remarked to the Countess: 'I like that single
rose better than all your elaborate *coiffures*.' He did not like
jewels, and shared the opinion of that noble lord who once
remarked coarsely: 'The devil himself could not recognize
an overdressed woman or a caparisoned horse.' The night
before, while toying with the Countess's pearl necklace (he
always had to have something in his hands when talking),
Saint-Clair had said: 'You are too pretty, Mathilde, to wear
jewels; they are only fit to hide defects.' This evening the
Countess had stripped herself of rings, necklaces, ear-rings,
and bracelets, for she noted even his most casual remarks.
He noticed, above everything else in a woman's dress, the
shoes she wore; and, like many other men, he had his little
fads on this point. A heavy shower had fallen before sunset,
and the grass was still very wet; in spite of this the Countess
had walked on the damp turf in silk stockings and black
satin slippers. . . . What if she were to fall ill?

'She loves me', said Saint-Clair to himself.

He sighed at himself and his folly, but smiled at Mathilde
in spite of himself, torn between his ill-humour and the
pleasure of seeing a pretty woman who tried to please him
in all those trifling ways which mean so much to lovers.

The Countess's face was radiant with love and a mischievous gaiety which made her more attractive than ever.
She took something out of a lacquered Japanese box and
held it out to him in her little closed hand.

'I broke your watch the other night', she said; 'here it is, mended.'

She handed the watch to him and looked at him tenderly yet mischievously, biting her lower lip as if to prevent herself from laughing. Oh, what beautiful white teeth she had, and how they gleamed against the bright pink of her lips! (A man looks very foolish when he responds coldly to the endearments of a pretty woman.)

Saint-Clair thanked her, took the watch, and was about to put it in his pocket.

'Look at it and open it', she continued. 'See if it has been properly repaired. You, who are so learned, you, who have been to the Polytechnic School, ought to be able to see.'

'Oh, I don't know much about such things', said Saint-Clair.

He opened the case in an absent-minded way and, to his surprise, he found a miniature portrait of Madame de Coursy painted on the interior. How could he go on sulking? His brow cleared; he thought no longer of Massigny; he only remembered that he was with a beautiful woman, and that this woman loved him.

The lark, 'that harbinger of dawn', was beginning to sing, and long bands of pale light stretched across the clouds in the east. It was the hour when Romeo said farewell to Juliet, the classic hour when all lovers have to part.

Saint-Clair was standing in front of a mantelpiece, the key of the garden gate in his hand, his eyes intently fixed on the Etruscan vase which we have already mentioned. In the depths of his soul he still bore it a grudge. However, he was in a much better humour, and the simple explanation that Thémines might have been lying was beginning to occur to him. While the Countess was wrapping a shawl round her head in order to go to the garden gate with him, he began to tap the detested vase with the key, first gently, then gradually increasing the force of his blows until it seemed as if he was going to smash it to pieces.

H

'Oh, do be careful!' Mathilde exclaimed. 'You're going to break my beautiful Etruscan vase.'

She snatched the key out of his hands.

Saint-Clair was very angry, but he resigned himself and turned his back on the mantelpiece to avoid temptation. Opening his watch, he began to examine the portrait which had just been given him.

'Who painted it?' he asked.

'Monsieur R——. You know, it was Massigny who brought him to my notice.' (After Massigny's visit to Rome he had discovered that he had exquisite taste in art, and had constituted himself the Maecenas of all young painters.) 'I really think this portrait is like me, though it is a little flattering.'

Saint-Clair felt an urge to fling the watch against the wall, to break it beyond all hope of repair. He controlled himself, however, and put it back in his pocket. Then he noticed that it was daylight, and, begging Mathilde not to come out with him, he left the house and strode across the garden. A few moments later he was alone in the countryside.

'Massigny! Massigny!' he exclaimed with concentrated fury. 'Can I never escape him? . . . No doubt the artist who painted this portrait painted another for Massigny. . . . What a fool I was to imagine for a moment that I was loved with a love equal to my own. . . . just because she had put a rose in her hair and was not wearing any jewels! . . . Why, she has a whole chest full. . . . Massigny, who never considered anything save a woman's appearance, was a great lover of jewellery! . . . Yes, there's no denying she's very good-natured; she knows how to conform to her lover's tastes. Damn it! I would rather a hundred times that she were a courtesan and had given herself for money. At least I could think that she loves me, seeing that she is my mistress and I am not paying her.'

Soon another still more distressing idea occurred to him. In a few weeks time the Countess would be out of mourning, and Saint-Clair had promised to marry her as soon as her

year of widowhood was over. He had promised. Promised?
No. He had never spoken of the matter, but such had been
his intention and the Countess had realized that. For him
this was as good as an oath. The previous day he would have
given a throne to hasten the time when he would acknow-
ledge his love publicly; now the very thought of marrying
the former mistress of Massigny made him shudder.

'Nevertheless, I must do it', he said to himself, 'and it
shall be done. No doubt the poor woman thought I knew
all about her former liaison; it seems to have been
common knowledge. Besides, she doesn't know me . . . she
cannot understand me. She thinks that I only love her as
Massigny loved her.'

Then he said to himself, not without a certain pride:

'For three months she has made me the happiest man
alive; such happiness is well worth the sacrifice of my whole
life.'

He did not go to bed but rode in the woods the whole of
the morning. In one of the pathways of the Bois de Verrières
he saw a man mounted on a fine English horse, who called
to him from a long way off, and promptly rode up to him.
It was Alphonse de Thémines. To a man in Saint-Clair's
state of mind solitude is particularly desirable, so that this
encounter with Thémines changed his bad humour into a
mute rage. Thémines did not notice his mood, or perhaps
took a malicious pleasure in thwarting him. He talked and
laughed and joked without noticing that he did not receive
any reply. Seeing a narrow track, Saint-Clair immediately
turned his horse into it, hoping the bore would not follow
him; but it was no use; bores do not abandon their prey so
easily. Thémines turned his horse's head and quickened his
pace in order to ride by Saint-Clair's side and continue the
conversation more easily.

I have said that the path was a narrow one. The two horses
could only just walk abreast along it. It was not, therefore,
to be wondered at that even so good a horseman as Thémines
should brush against Saint-Clair's foot as he rode along

beside him. The latter, whose anger was at boiling point, could not contain himself any longer. He rose in his stirrups and struck Thémines's horse sharply across the nose with his whip.

'What the devil is the matter with you, Auguste?' cried Thémines. 'Why do you strike my horse?'

'Why do you follow me?' retorted Saint-Clair in a voice like thunder.

'Have you lost your senses, Saint-Clair? You forget to whom you are talking.'

'I know perfectly well that I'm talking to a fool.'

'Saint-Clair! . . . You must be mad, I think. Listen to me. Tomorrow you will either apologize to me, or you will account for your insolent conduct.'

'Tomorrow then, Monsieur.'

Thémines stopped his horse; Saint-Clair pushed his on, and soon disappeared into the wood.

He felt calmer now. He was superstitious enough to believe in premonitions. He felt sure he would be killed the next day, and in that event his problem would be solved. Only one more day to live through, and then he would have no more anxieties, no more torments to endure. He went home and sent his servant with a note to Colonel Beaujeu. He wrote a few letters, dined with a good appetite, and arrived punctually at the little garden gate at half past eight.

'What is the matter with you today, Auguste?' asked the Countess. 'You are unusually gay, and yet with all your pleasantries you cannot make me laugh. Last night you were just a trifle peevish, and I was the gay one! We have changed roles today. For my part, I have a splitting headache.'

'Dearest, I admit that I was very tedious yesterday, but today I have been riding, I have taken exercise, and I feel in splendid form.'

'As for me, I overslept this morning, I rose late, and I had some bad dreams last night.'

'Ah! Dreams? Do you believe in dreams?'

'What nonsense!'

'I believe in them. I am willing to wager that you had a dream which foretold some tragic event.'

'Heavens, I never remember my dreams. Now I come to think of it, though, I remember . . . that I saw Massigny in my dream; so you can see it was not very entertaining.'

'Massigny! But I should have thought you would have been delighted to see him again?'

'Poor Massigny!'

'Why "poor Massigny"?'

'Please tell me, Auguste, what is the matter with you to-night? Your smile has something diabolical about it, and you seem to be making fun of yourself.'

'Ah! Now you are treating me as badly as your old dowager friends treat me.'

'Yes, Auguste, you have the same expression today that you wear when you are with people you don't like.'

'That is unkind of you. Come, give me your hand.'

He kissed her hand with ironical gallantry, and they gazed hard at each other for a minute. Saint-Clair was the first to drop his eyes.

'How difficult it is', he exclaimed, 'to live in this world without being thought ill of! One ought never to talk of anything but the weather and hunting, or else discuss with your old ladies the finances of their charity committees.'

He picked up a piece of paper from a table.

'Look, here is a bill from your fine laundress. Let us chat about that, dearest; then you cannot say I am ill-tempered.'

'Really, Auguste, you amaze me. . . .'

'This handwriting reminds me of a letter I found this morning. I must explain that I have fits of tidiness now and then, and I was sorting out my papers. Well, I found a love-letter from a dressmaker with whom I was in love at sixteen. She had her own special way of writing every word and her style was on a par with her spelling. Well, I was silly enough at that time to consider it unworthy of me to have a mistress who could not write as well as Madame de Sévigné, and I left her abruptly. Reading this letter again today I saw that that dressmaker was really in love with me.'

'Really! A woman you kept?'

'In fine style—on fifty francs a month. But I could not afford any more, as my guardian only made me a modest allowance, for he said that young men who had money ruined themselves and others.'

'What became of that woman?'

'How should I know? . . . Probably she died in a workhouse.'

'Auguste . . . if that were true you would not look so unconcerned.'

'Well, then, to tell you the truth, she married "a decent fellow", and when I came of age I gave her a small dowry.'

'How kind you are! . . . But why do you try to make yourself out to be so wicked?'

'Oh, I am good enough. . . . The more I think of it, the more I am convinced that that woman really did love me. . . . But at that time I was incapable of discerning true feeling in a ridiculous form.'

'You ought to have brought me your letter. I shouldn't have been jealous. . . . We women have a finer tact than you, and we can tell at a glance, from the style of a letter, whether the writer is sincere, or feigning a passion he doesn't really feel.'

'Yet how many times have you allowed yourself to be taken in by fools and fops!'

As he spoke he looked at the Etruscan vase, and in both his eyes and voice there was something sinister which Mathilde did not notice.

'Come now, all you men wish to pass for Don Juans. You fancy you are making dupes when often you have only met a Doña Juana, who is even more cunning than yourselves.'

'I am ready to grant that with your superior minds you ladies can smell a fool a mile off. And I don't doubt that your friend Massigny, who was both a fool and a fop, died a virgin and a martyr.'

'Massigny? He wasn't such a fool; besides, there are plenty of silly women. I must tell you a story about Massigny. But haven't I told it to you already?'

'Never', replied Saint-Clair in a trembling voice.

'Massigny fell in love with me on his return from Italy. My husband knew him and introduced him to me as a man of taste and culture. Those two were just made for each other. Massigny was most attentive to me at first; he gave me some water-colour sketches, which he had bought from Schroth, as his own work, and talked to me of music and art in the most amusingly superior manner. One day he sent me an incredible letter. He said, among other things, that I was the most respectable woman in Paris; that was why he wished to be my lover. I showed the letter to my cousin Julie. We were a couple of madcaps at that time, and we decided to play a trick on him. One evening we had several visitors, including Massigny. My cousin said to me: "I am going to read you a declaration of love which I received this morning." She took the letter and read it in the midst of roars of laughter. . . . Poor Massigny! . . .'

Saint-Clair fell on his knees with a cry of joy. He seized the Countess's hand and covered it with tears and kisses. Mathilde was surprised beyond belief, and thought at first he was feeling ill. Saint-Clair could only murmur: 'Forgive me! Forgive me!' When at last he rose to his feet he was radiant; he was happier at that moment than on the day when Mathilde had said to him for the first time: 'I love you'.

'I am the guiltiest and most stupid of men', he cried; 'for two days I have suspected you . . . and never given you a chance to explain. . . .'

'You suspected me? . . . Of what?'

'Oh, what a fool I was! . . . They told me you had been in love with Massigny, and . . .'

'Massigny!' and she began to laugh; then, promptly becoming serious again, 'Auguste,' she said, 'how could you be so foolish as to harbour such suspicions, and be so hypocritical as to hide them from me?'

Her eyes filled with tears.

'I implore you to forgive me.'

'Of course I forgive you, beloved. . . . But first let me swear to you . . .'

'Oh, I believe you, I believe you: don't say another word.'

'But, in Heaven's name, what put such an improbable idea into your head?'

'Nothing, nothing in the world except my stupid temper . . . and . . . well, that Etruscan vase which I knew Massigny had given you.'

The Countess clasped her hands together in amazement, and then, bursting out laughing, she exclaimed:

'My Etruscan vase! My Etruscan vase!'

Saint-Clair could not help laughing himself, although great tears were rolling down his cheeks. He clasped Mathilde in his arms.

'I will not let you go', he said, 'until you forgive me.'

'Yes, I forgive you, idiot that you are', she replied, kissing him tenderly. 'You have made me very happy today; it is the first time I have seen you shed tears, and I thought that you were incapable of weeping.'

Then, breaking away from his arms, she seized the Etruscan vase and broke it into a thousand pieces on the floor. It was a rare work, painted in three colours, and represented the fight between a Lapitha and a Centaur.

For a few hours Saint-Clair was the happiest and the most shamefaced of men.

'Well,' said Roquantin to Colonel Beaujeu, when he met him in the evening at Tortoni's, 'is the news true?'

'Only too true, my friend', answered the Colonel sadly.

'Tell me, how did it go?'

'Oh, Saint-Clair began by telling me that he was in the wrong, but that he wished to stand up to Thémines's fire before begging his pardon. I could do nothing but approve of his decision. Thémines wished to draw lots who should fire first. Saint-Clair insisted that Thémines should. Thémines fired; I saw Saint-Clair spin round once and then fall stone dead. I have often noticed, in the case of soldiers I have seen shot, this strange spinning motion which precedes death.'

'How very extraordinary!' said Roquantin. 'And what did Thémines do?'

'Oh, what is usual on these occasions: he threw his pistol on the ground with an air of regret. He threw it so hard, in fact, that he broke the hammer. It was an English pistol, a Manton. I don't know if he will be able to find a gunsmith in Paris who can make him another like it.'

The Countess shut herself up in her country house for three whole years without seeing anyone; she stayed there winter and summer, scarcely going out of her room, and waited on by a mulatto woman who knew of her liaison with Saint-Clair and to whom she barely addressed a couple of words a day. At the end of three years her cousin Julie returned from a long voyage. She forced her way into the house and found poor Mathilde so thin and pale that she thought she was looking at the ghost of the woman she had left behind beautiful and full of life. She managed with difficulty to prevail upon her to leave her retreat and took her to Hyères. The Countess languished there for three or four months and then died of consumption, brought on by what Dr. M——, who attended her, called domestic worries.

1830

The Game of Backgammon

THE sails hung motionless, clinging to the masts; the sea was as smooth as glass; the heat was stifling, the calm disheartening.

During a sea voyage the opportunities for amusement open to passengers on board ship are soon exhausted. People who have spent four months together in a wooden house one hundred and twenty feet long know each other only too well. When you see the first lieutenant coming towards you, you know that first of all he is going to talk to you about Rio de Janeiro, where he hails from, and then of the famous Pont d'Essling, which he saw made by the Naval Guards, to which he belonged. After a fortnight you even know his favourite expressions, the punctuation of his sentences, and the different intonations of his voice. When has he ever failed to pause sadly after mentioning the Emperor for the first time in his story? . . . And he invariably adds: 'If only you had seen him then!!!' (three exclamation marks to denote his admiration). And the incident of the trumpeter's horse, and the bullet which ricocheted and carried away a cartridge-box containing seven thousand five hundred francs in gold and jewellery, etc., etc.! The second lieutenant is a great politician; he comments every day upon the last number of the *Constitutionnel* which he has brought from Brest, or, if he leaves the sublime heights of politics to descend to literature, he will regale you with the plot of the last farce he has seen. Heaven preserve us! . . . The paymaster has a very interesting story. How he delighted us the first time he told us about his escape from the prison-ship at Cadiz, but at the twentieth repetition, upon my word, it is barely endurable! . . . And the ensigns and the midshipmen! . . . The recollection of their conversation makes my hair stand on end. Generally speaking, the captain is the least boring person on board. In his position as despotic commander he is in a state of undeclared hostilities against the whole company; he annoys and oppresses at times, but there is a certain amount of pleasure to be gained by inveighing against him. If he has some irritating fad, his subordinates have the pleasure of seeing him in a ridiculous light, and this is some slight consolation.

On board the vessel on which I was sailing the officers were all good fellows, the best of company, devoted to one another, but all unutterably bored. The captain was the gentlest of men and, what is very rare, was nothing of a busybody. It was always with regret that he exercised his dictatorial power. But, in spite of everything, the voyage seemed terribly long, to me, especially when a calm set in only a few days before we made land! . . .

One day after dinner, which want of employment had made us spin out as long as was humanly possible, we were all assembled on deck, waiting for the monotonous but ever majestic spectacle of a sunset at sea. Some were smoking, others were re-reading for the twentieth time one of the thirty volumes which comprised our wretched library; all were yawning their heads off. An ensign sitting next to me was amusing himself, with all the gravity worthy of a serious occupation, by letting the poniard, worn ordinarily by naval officers in undress, fall, point downwards, on the planks of the deck. It was as amusing a pastime as any other, and one which required some skill to make the point stick in the wood quite perpendicularly. I wanted to follow the ensign's example, and, not having a poniard of my own, I tried to borrow the captain's, but he refused to lend it to me. He was singularly attached to that weapon, and it would have vexed him to see it put to such a futile use. It had formerly belonged to a brave officer who had been mortally wounded in the last war. I guessed that a story would be forthcoming, and I was not mistaken. The captain began without waiting to be asked, and the officers who stood around us, and who

knew the misfortunes of Lieutenant Roger by heart,
promptly beat a prudent retreat. Here is the captain's story,
more or less in his own words:

Roger was three years older than I when I first knew him;
he was a lieutenant and I was an ensign. He was quite one of
the best officers among us; he was, moreover, good-natured,
talented, intelligent, and well educated; in a word, he was a
charming young man. Unfortunately, he was rather proud
and sensitive; this arose, I think, from the fact of his being
an illegitimate child, and his fear that his birth might make
people look down on him; but, to tell the truth, the greatest
of all his faults was a passionate and ever-present desire to
take the lead wherever he was. His father, whom he had
never seen, made him an allowance which would have been
more than enough for his needs, if Roger had not been the
soul of generosity. All that he had was at the service of his
friends. When he drew his quarterly allowance, anybody
who went to see him with a sad and anxious face would be
met with the question:

'Why, old fellow, what's the matter? You look as if you
would find it hard to make your pockets jingle if you slapped
them; come, here is my purse, take what you need and
come and have dinner with me.'

A very pretty young actress called Gabrielle came to
Brest, and quickly made conquests among the seamen and
officers of the garrison. She was not a perfect beauty, but
she had a good figure, fine eyes, a dainty foot, and a saucy
air; these things are all very delightful when one is between
the latitudes of twenty and twenty-five years of age. She was
said, in addition, to be the most capricious creature of her
sex, and her style of acting did not belie this reputation.
Sometimes she acted enchantingly, and anyone would have
taken her for a *comédienne* of the highest order; the following
day she would be cold and lifeless in the very same play; she
would reel off her part as a child recites its catechism. But
more than anything else it was the story told of her which I

am about to relate that interested our young men. It seems
that she had been kept in sumptuous style in Paris by a
senator, who, as the saying goes, committed all sorts of
follies for her sake. One day this man put his hat on in her
house; she asked him to take it off, and even complained
that he was showing a want of respect towards her. The
senator burst out laughing, shrugged his shoulders, and said,
as he settled himself in an arm-chair: 'The least I can do is
to make myself at home in the house of a whore I pay
for.' A resounding smack from Gabrielle's white hand
paid him back for his reply and sent his hat flying to the
other end of the room. The result was a complete break
between them. Bankers and generals had made considerable offers to the lady, but she had refused them all and
become an actress, so that she could, as she put it, live in-
dependently.

When Roger saw her and learnt her story, he decided that
she must be his, and with the somewhat brutal directness
with which we sailors are reproached, he took the following
steps to show her how much he was affected by her charms.
He bought the rarest and loveliest flowers to be found in
Brest, made them into a bouquet which he tied with a
beautiful pink ribbon, and in the knot he carefully placed a
roll of twenty-five napoleons, all he possessed for the time
being. I remember accompanying him backstage during an
interval. He paid Gabrielle a brief compliment on the grace
with which she wore her costume, offered her the bouquet,
and asked leave to call on her. He managed to get through
all this in a few words.

As long as Gabrielle only saw the flowers and the handsome young man who offered them to her, she smiled at
him, accompanying her smile with a most gracious curtsy;
but when she held the bouquet in her hands and felt the
weight of the gold, her face changed more rapidly than the
surface of the sea when stirred up by a tropical hurricane;
and certainly she was scarcely less spiteful, for she hurled
the bouquet and the napoleons with all her strength at my

poor friend's head, so that he carried the marks of it on his face for more than a week. The stage-manager's bell rang and Gabrielle went on and acted all awry.

Covered with confusion, Roger picked up his bouquet and roll of gold, went to a café, offered the bouquet (but not the money) to the girl behind the bar, and tried to forget the cruel actress in a glass of punch. But he did not succeed, and, in spite of his vexation at not being able to show himself in public with his black eye, he fell madly in love with the angry Gabrielle. He wrote her twenty letters a day, and such letters!—submissive, tender, respectful letters such as might have been addressed to a princess. The first were returned to him unopened, and the rest received no answer. Roger, however, retained some hope, until we discovered that the theatre orange-seller wrapped up her oranges in Roger's love-letters, which Gabrielle gave her as a refinement of malice. This was a terrible blow to our friend's pride; but his passion did not diminish. He talked of asking the actress to marry him, and threatened to blow his brains out when we told him that the Minister for the Navy would never give his consent.

While all this was going on, the officers of a regiment of the line quartered in Brest tried to make Gabrielle repeat a vaudeville couplet, and she refused out of sheer stubbornness. The officers and the actress both remained so obstinate that the former hissed until the curtain was dropped, and the latter fainted. You know what the pit of a theatre in a garrison town is like. The officers agreed among themselves to hiss her without stopping the next day and the following days, and not to allow her to play a single part until she had made humble amends for her bad behaviour. Roger had not been present at this performance; but the same evening he heard of the scandal which had put the whole theatre in an uproar, and also of the plans for revenge which were being hatched for the next day. He immediately made up his mind what he would do.

When Gabrielle made her appearance the next night an

ear-splitting noise of catcalls and whistles came from the officers' seats. Roger, who had deliberately placed himself near the trouble-makers, got up and harangued the noisiest of them in such scathing language that all their fury was promptly turned on him. He then took his notebook from his pocket, and, with the utmost sang-froid wrote down the names called out to him from all sides; he would have arranged to fight with the whole regiment if a great many naval officers had not intervened, out of *esprit de corps*, and taken on most of his adversaries. The hubbub was indescribable.

The whole garrison was confined to barracks for several days, but when our freedom was restored to us, there was a terrible score to settle. About sixty of us met on the duelling-ground. Roger, alone, fought three officers in succession; he killed one, and badly wounded the other two, without receiving a scratch. I, for my part, was less fortunate; a confounded lieutenant, who had been a fencing master, gave me a deep thrust in the chest which nearly finished me off. The duel, or rather battle, was a fine sight, I can tell you. The Navy had the best of it, and the regiment was obliged to leave Brest.

As you may imagine, our superior officers did not overlook the author of the quarrel. There was a guard outside his door for a fortnight.

When his term of arrest was over I came out of hospital and went to see him. Imagine my surprise when I entered his room and found him sitting at breakfast *tête-à-tête* with Gabrielle. They seemed to have been on close terms for some time, for they already called each other *tu* and drank out of the same glass. Roger introduced me to his mistress as his best friend, and told her I had been wounded in the skirmish of which she had been the basic cause. That beautiful girl then condescended to kiss me, for her sympathies were thoroughly martial.

They spent three months together in perfect happiness, and never left each other for a moment. Gabrielle seemed to

love him to distraction, and Roger confessed that he had
never known love before meeting Gabrielle.

One day a Dutch frigate came into the harbour. The
officers invited us to dinner. We drank copiously of all
sorts of wines; and when the cloth was removed, not knowing what to do, for our hosts spoke very bad French, we
began to play. The Dutchmen seemed to have plenty of
money; and their first lieutenant especially wanted to play
for such high stakes that none of us cared to take him on.
But Roger, who did not play as a rule, felt it incumbent on
him on this occasion to uphold the honour of his country.
So he played for the stakes that the Dutch lieutenant pro-
posed. At first he won, then he lost, and after several changes
of fortune they separated without any decisive result. We
returned this dinner, and invited the Dutch officers. Again
we played, and Roger and the lieutenant got to grips once
more. In short, they played for several days, meeting either
in cafés or on board ship; they tried all sorts of games,
especially backgammon, steadily increasing their stakes until
they came to the point of playing for twenty-five napoleons
a game. This was an enormous sum for poverty-stricken
officers like us—more than two months' pay! At the end of
a week Roger had lost every penny he possessed, and more
than three or four thousand francs which he had borrowed
right and left.

As you may imagine, Roger and Gabrielle had ended up
by sharing bed and purse; that is to say that Roger, who had
just received a large payment in the way of prize-money, had
contributed ten or twenty times more than the actress.
However, he still considered that this sum belonged chiefly
to his mistress, and he had only kept back for his own
expenses about fifty napoleons. All the same, he had been
obliged to draw on this reserve to go on playing, and
Gabrielle did not raise the slightest objection.

The housekeeping money went the same way as his pocket-
money. Soon Roger was reduced to playing his last twenty-
five napoleons. He concentrated all his attention on the

game, so it was lengthy and hotly contested. The moment
came when Roger, who held the dice-box, had only one
chance left to win; I think he had to get a six and a four. The
night was far advanced, and an officer who had been watching them play for a long time, had ended up by falling asleep
in an arm-chair. The Dutchman was tired and drowsy;
moreover, he had drunk a great deal of punch. Roger alone
was wide awake and a prey to the most violent despair.
He trembled as he threw the dice. He threw them so roughly
on to the board that the shock knocked a candle over on to
the floor. The Dutchman turned his head first towards the
candle, which had just spattered his new trousers with wax,
and then looked at the dice. They showed six and four.
Roger, who was as pale as death, received the twenty-five
napoleons, and they went on playing. Chance began to
favour my unlucky friend, for all that he made blunder after
blunder and secured points as if he had wanted to lose. The
Dutch lieutenant refused to give in, and doubled and
quadrupled his stakes; he lost every time. I can see him now
—a tall, fair, phlegmatic fellow, whose face seemed to be
made of wax. At last he got up, having lost forty thousand
francs, and paid them over without his features betraying
the least trace of emotion.

'We won't count tonight', Roger said to him. 'You were
half asleep. I don't want your money.'

'You are joking', replied the phlegmatic Dutchman; 'I
played very well, but the dice were against me. I am sure I
can easily beat you another time. Good night!'

And he went out.

We learnt the next day that, driven to despair by his losses,
he had blown out his brains in his room, after drinking a
bowl of punch.

The forty thousand francs that Roger had won from him
were spread out on the table, and Gabrielle gazed at them
with a smile of satisfaction.

'See how rich we are!' she said. 'What shall we do with
all this money?'

I

Roger made no reply; he seemed stunned since the Dutchman's death.

'We must do a thousand crazy things', she went on. 'Money won so easily ought to be spent the same way. Let us buy a carriage, and snap our fingers at the Maritime Prefect and his wife. I want diamonds and cashmere shawls. Ask for some leave, and let's go to Paris; we'll never manage to spend so much money here!'

She stopped to look at Roger, who, with his eyes fixed on the floor, and his head resting on his hand, had not heard a word; he seemed to be a prey to the gloomiest thoughts.

'What on earth's the matter with you, Roger?' she cried, resting her hand on his shoulder. 'You are sulking, I think. I can't get a word out of you.'

'I am very unhappy', he said at last, with a stifled sigh.

'Unhappy! Why, I do believe you regret having fleeced that fat *mynheer*.'

He raised his head and looked at her with haggard eyes.

'What does it matter', she went on, 'if he did take the thing tragically and blow out what few brains he had? I don't pity losing players; and his money is certainly better in our hands than in his. He would have wasted it on drink and tobacco, while we will spend it on a thousand extravagant follies, each more elegant than the last.'

Roger walked about the room with his head hanging, his eyes half closed and filled with tears. You would have been sorry for him if you had seen him.

'You know,' Gabrielle said to him, 'anyone who did not know how romantically sensitive you are might imagine you had cheated.'

'And what if that were the truth?' he cried in hollow tones, stopping in front of her.

'Nonsense!' she answered with a smile. 'You aren't clever enough to cheat at play.'

'Yes, I cheated, Gabrielle; I cheated like the wretch I am.'

She understood from his agitation that he was speaking only too truly. She sat down on a couch and remained silent for some time.

'I would rather you had killed ten men than cheated at play', she said at last in a very troubled voice.

There was a deathly silence for half an hour. They were both sitting on the same sofa, and did not look at each other once. Roger got up first and wished her good night in a calm voice.

'Good night', she replied in cold, hard tones.

Roger has since told me that he would have killed himself that very day if he had not been afraid that his comrades would have guessed the reason for his suicide. He did not wish his memory to be disgraced.

Gabrielle was as gay as usual the next day. She seemed to have already forgotten the confidence of the previous evening. But Roger had become gloomy, capricious, and morose. He scarcely left his room, avoided his friends, and often spent days on end without saying a word to his mistress. I attributed his melancholy to an honourable but excessive sensitiveness, and I tried several times to console him; but he rebuffed me, affecting a supreme indifference towards his unhappy partner. One day he even inveighed against the Dutch nation in violent terms, and maintained that there was not a single honourable man in Holland. All the same, he secretly tried to find out about the Dutch lieutenant's relatives; but no one could give him any information about them.

Six weeks after that unlucky game of backgammon, Roger found a note in Gabrielle's rooms, written by an admirer who thanked her for the favours she had bestowed on him. Gabrielle was the very personification of untidiness, and she had left the note in question on her mantelpiece. I do not know whether she had been unfaithful to Roger or not, but he believed that she had, and his anger was frightful. His love and a remnant of pride were the only feelings which still attached him to life, and the stronger of these sentiments was thus about to be suddenly destroyed. He heaped insults on the proud actress, and, considering his violent temper, I do not know how he refrained from beating her.

'No doubt', he said to her, 'this puppy has given you plenty of money. It's the only thing you love. You would give yourself to the dirtiest of our seamen if he had the money to pay you.'

'Why not?' retorted the actress icily. 'Yes, I would sell myself to a seaman, but . . . *I* would not rob him.'

Roger uttered a cry of rage. Trembling, he drew his dagger, and for a moment looked at Gabrielle with the eyes of a madman; then, gathering all his strength, he threw the weapon at her feet and rushed out of the room to prevent himself from the temptation besetting him.

That same evening I passed his lodgings at a late hour, and, seeing his light burning, I went in to borrow a book. I found him busy writing. He did not put himself out, and scarcely seemed to notice my presence in his room. I sat down by his desk and studied his features; they had changed so much that anyone else but I would hardly have recognized him. All at once I noticed a letter already sealed on his desk, addressed to myself. I opened it straight away. In it Roger informed me that he intended to put an end to himself, and gave me various instructions to carry out. While I was reading, he went on writing without paying any attention to me: he was bidding farewell to Gabrielle. You can imagine my astonishment, and what I felt bound to say to him, thunderstruck as I was by his decision.

'What, you want to kill yourself—you who are so happy?'

'My dear fellow,' he said, as he sealed his letter, 'you know nothing about it; you don't know me; I am a scoundrel; I am so guilty that a prostitute has the power to insult me; and I am so conscious of my baseness that I cannot bring myself to beat her.'

Then he told me the story of the game of backgammon, and everything that you already know. As I listened, I was at least as moved as he was. I did not know what to say to him; with tears in my eyes, I pressed his hands, but I could not speak. Finally, the idea came to me to try and show him that he could not reproach himself with having intentionally caused the ruin of the Dutchman, and that, after all, he had only made him lose, by his ... cheating ..., twenty-five napoleons.

'So', he cried, with bitter irony, 'I am a petty thief and not a great one. I, who was so ambitious, am nothing but a scurvy little scoundrel!'

And he roared with laughter.

I burst into tears.

Suddenly the door opened; a woman came in and threw herself into his arms; it was Gabrielle.

'Forgive me!' she cried, clasping him tightly. 'Forgive me! I know now that I love only you; and I love you more now than if you had not done what you blame yourself for. If you like, I will steal; I have stolen before now.... Yes, I have stolen; I once stole a gold watch.... What could be worse than that?'

Roger shook his head incredulously, but his face seemed to brighten.

'No, my poor child', he said, gently repulsing her. 'I must kill myself. I am suffering so greatly that I cannot bear my grief.'

'Very well, then, if you intend to die, Roger, I shall die with you. What is life to me without you? I have plenty of courage; I have fired rifles; I shall kill myself like anyone else. Besides, I have played at tragedy and am used to it.'

At first there were tears in her eyes, but this last idea amused her, and even Roger could not help smiling with her.

'You are laughing, my love', she cried, clapping her hands and kissing him; 'you will not kill yourself.'

And she went on kissing him, first crying, and then laughing, then swearing like a sailor; for she was not the sort of woman to flinch at strong language.

In the meantime I had taken possession of Roger's pistols and poniard; and I said to him:

'My dear Roger, you have a mistress and a friend who love you. Believe me, there can still be some happiness for you in this life.' I embraced him and went out, leaving him alone with Gabrielle.

I do not believe we should have succeeded in doing anything more than delaying his fatal plan if he had not received an order from the Minister to set out as first lieutenant on board a frigate bound for duty in the Indian seas—if it could first cross the lines of the English squadron blockading the port. It was a dangerous venture. I put it to him that it would be better to die nobly by an English bullet than to put an inglorious end to his life himself, without rendering any service to his country. So he promised to live. He distributed half the forty thousand francs to disabled sailors or to seamen's widows and orphans; the rest he gave to Gabrielle, who at first swore to use the money only for charitable purposes. She fully meant to keep her word, poor girl; but enthusiasm with her was short-lived. I have heard since that she gave a few thousand francs to the poor, but she spent the remainder on clothes for herself.

Roger and I boarded the fine frigate *La Galatée*; our men were brave, well-trained, and well-disciplined; but our commander was an idiot, who thought himself a Jean Bart because he could swear better than any trooper, because he spoke atrocious French, and because he had never studied the theory of his profession, the practice of which he understood only very indifferently. However, fate favoured us at the outset. We got out of the roadstead unscathed, thanks to a gust of wind which compelled the blockading squadron to give us a wide birth, and we began our cruise by burning an English sloop and an East Indiaman off the coast of Portugal.

We sailed slowly on towards the Indian seas, hampered by contrary winds and the bad navigation of our captain, whose incompetence increased the danger of our cruise.

Sometimes pursued by superior forces, sometimes pursuing merchant ships ourselves, we did not pass a single day without some fresh adventure. But neither the dangerous life we were leading, nor the fatigue caused him by the irksome duties which fell to him, could distract Roger from the sad thoughts which unceasingly haunted him. He who was once considered the most brilliant and active officer in our port now confined himself simply to doing his duty. As soon as he was off duty he would shut himself in his cabin without either books or papers, and the unhappy man passed whole hours lying on his bunk, unable to sleep.

One day, noticing his depression, I ventured to say to him:

'Dammit, my dear fellow, you're upsetting yourself over nothing. Granted you cheated a fat Dutchman out of twenty-five napoleons, but you show as much remorse as though you had taken over a million. Now, tell me, when you were the lover of the wife of the Prefect of ——, did you feel any remorse at all? Yet she was worth more than twenty-five napoleons.'

He turned over on his mattress without a word.

'After all,' I continued, 'your crime, since you persist in calling it a crime, had an honourable motive and came from a noble soul.'

He turned his head and glared at me.

'Yes, for if you had lost what would have become of Gabrielle? The poor girl would have sold everything she had for you. . . . If you had lost she would have been reduced to poverty. . . . It was for her, out of love for her, that you cheated. There are people who kill for love . . . who kill themselves. . . . You, my dear Roger, did more. For a man of our sort, it takes more courage to . . . steal, to put it baldly, than to commit suicide.'

('Now, perhaps,' the captain interrupted his story to say, 'I appear ridiculous to you. I assure you that my friendship for Roger endowed me at that time with an eloquence which I can no longer summon up today; and, devil take it, in

saying what I did I spoke in good earnest, and I believed
all I said. Ah, I was young then!')

Roger did not answer for some time; then he held out his
hand to me.

'My dear fellow,' he said, appearing to make a great effort
of self-control, 'you think too well of me. I am a cowardly
wretch. When I cheated that Dutchman, my only thought
was to win twenty-five napoleons, that was all. I never
thought of Gabrielle, and that is why I despise myself. . . .
I, to hold my honour in less esteem than twenty-five
napoleons! . . . What baseness! Yes, I should be happy if I
could tell myself I had stolen to save Gabrielle from poverty.
No! . . . No! I did not think of her. . . . I was not in love at
that moment. . . . I was a gambler. . . . I was a thief. . . . I
stole money to possess it myself . . . and that deed has so
degraded and debased me that now I have no courage left
nor love. . . . I live, and I do not think any longer of
Gabrielle. . . . I am finished.'

He seemed so wretched that if he had asked me to hand
him his pistols to kill himself I do believe I should have
given them to him.

One Friday, that day of ill omen, we sighted a big English
frigate, the *Alcestis*, which gave chase to us. She carried
fifty-eight guns, and we had only thirty-eight. We put on all
sail to escape from her, but her pace was faster than ours.
She was gaining on us every minute, and it was obvious that
before nightfall we should be obliged to engage in an un-
equal battle. Our captain called Roger to his cabin, where
they consulted together for over a quarter of an hour.
Roger came up on deck again, took me by the arm, and
drew me aside.

'In two hours' time', he said, 'we shall be engaged. That
good fellow who is strutting the quarter-deck over there has
lost his wits. There were two courses to choose from; the
first, and the more honourable, was to let the enemy come
up to us, then board the ship boldly with a hundred or so
determined men; the other course, which is not bad, but

rather cowardly, would be to lighten ourselves by throwing some of our guns overboard. Then we could hug the coast of Africa, which we can see over there on the port side. The English captain would soon be obliged to give up the chase, for fear of running aground; but our . . . captain is neither a coward nor a hero. He will let himself be disabled by long-range fire, and after a few hours' fight he will honourably lower his flag. So much the worse for you: the Portsmouth hulks are waiting for you. I have no desire to see them.'

'Possibly', I said, 'our first shots will damage the enemy sufficiently to compel him to abandon the chase.'

'Listen, I do not mean to be taken prisoner; I want to get myself killed. It is time I put an end to it all. If by bad luck I am only wounded, give me your word of honour that you will throw me overboard. It is the proper death-bed for a good sailor.'

'What nonsense', I exclaimed; 'and what a task to give me!'

'You will be fulfilling the duty of a true friend. You know I must die. I only agreed not to take my own life in the hope of being killed; you must remember that. Come, promise me this; if you refuse, I shall go and ask this service from the boatswain's mate, who won't refuse.'

After reflecting for some time, I said to him:

'I give you my word to do what you wish, provided that you are mortally wounded, with no hope of recovery. In that case, I agree to spare you further suffering.'

'I shall be mortally wounded or I shall be killed outright.'

He held out his hand to me, and I shook it firmly. After that he was calmer, and his face even lit up with a kind of martial cheerfulness.

About three o'clock in the afternoon the enemy's guns began to hit our rigging. We then took in some of our sails, crossed the bows of the *Alcestis*, and opened a running fire, which the English returned vigorously. After about an hour's fighting our captain, who did nothing at the right moment, decided to try to board the enemy; but we already had a great many dead and wounded, and the remainder of our crew had lost some of their spirit. Our rigging, besides, had suffered severely, and our masts were badly damaged. Just as we were spreading our sails to approach the English vessel, our mainmast, which no longer had anything to support it, fell with a terrible din. The *Alcestis* took advantage of the confusion into which this accident threw us. She came broadside up to our stern and opened fire on us within half a pistol-range; she raked our unfortunate frigate with shot, fore and aft, and we could reply with only two small guns. At that moment I was standing near Roger, who was busy having the shrouds cut which still held the fallen mast. I felt him grip my arm hard; I turned round and saw him lying on his back on the deck, covered with blood. He had received a charge of grape-shot in the stomach.

'What are we to do, lieutenant?' cried the captain, running up.

'Nail our flag to this stump of mast and go down fighting.'

The captain left him at that, for he did not particularly relish the advice.

'Come,' Roger said to me, 'remember your promise.'

'It's nothing,' I said, 'you will get over it.'

'Throw me overboard!' he cried, swearing horribly, and seizing me by my coat-tails. 'You see well enough that I cannot recover. Throw me into the sea; I don't want to see our colours struck.'

Two sailors came up to carry him below.

'To your guns, you scoundrels!' he shouted. 'Use grape-shot, and aim at the deck. And as for you, if you fail to keep your word I will curse you as the most cowardly and vile of men!'

His wound was certainly mortal. I saw the captain call a midshipman and give him the order to strike our colours.

'Shake hands with me', I said to Roger.

And at the very moment that our colours were struck. . . .

'Captain, a whale on the port side!' interrupted an ensign, running up to us.

'A whale?' cried the captain, carried away with joy and leaving his story unfinished. 'Quick, launch the longboat! All the longboats! Bring the harpoons and lines!...'

I never found out how poor Lieutenant Roger died.

1830

Lokis

FROM THE MS. OF PROFESSOR WITTEMBACH

'Théodore,' said Professor Wittembach, 'please hand me that notebook, bound in parchment, on the second shelf above my writing-desk—no, not that one, but the small octavo volume. I copied all the notes from my diary for 1866 into it—at least those relating to Count Szemioth.'

The Professor put on his glasses, and, in the midst of the most profound silence, read out the following:

LOKIS

with this Lithuanian proverb as an epigraph:

> Miszka su Lokiu
> Abu du tokiu.[1]

*   *   *

When the first translation of the Holy Scriptures into the Lithuanian language appeared in London, I published an article in the *Scientific and Literary Gazette* of Königsberg in which, while rendering full justice to the efforts of the learned interpreter and to the pious motives of the Bible Society, I pointed out a few slight errors and observed, moreover, that this version could only be useful to one portion of the Lithuanian population. The dialect used in the translation is indeed hardly intelligible to the inhabitants of the districts where the *Jomaïtic* tongue, commonly called *Jmoude*, is spoken, namely, in the Palatinate of Samogitia. This language is, perhaps, even closer to Sanskrit than High Lithuanian. In spite of the furious criticisms which this observa-

---

[1] 'The two together make a pair'; word for word, Mike (Michael) with Lokis, both the same. *Michaelium cum Lokide, ambo* [*duo*] *ipsissimi.*

tion drew down upon me from a certain well-known professor of Dorpat University, it enlightened the honourable members of the Committee of the Bible Society, and they lost no time in making me a flattering offer to direct and supervise the translation of the Gospel of St. Matthew into Samogitian. I was too much occupied at the time with my researches into Trans-Uralian dialects to undertake a more extended work comprising all four Gospels. So, postponing my marriage to Mademoiselle Gertrude Weber, I went to Kowno (Kaunas) for the purpose of collecting all the linguistic records, whether printed or in manuscript, of Jmoude, that I could lay hands on. I did not overlook, of course, the folk ballads (*daïnos*) and the tales or legends (*pasakos*) which would furnish me with material for a Jomaïtic vocabulary, a work which must necessarily precede that of translation.

I had been given a letter of introduction to the young Count Michel Szemioth, whose father, I was told, had once been in possession of the famous *Catechismus Samogiticus* of Father Lawiçki. It was so rare that its very existence has been disputed, notably by the Dorpat professor whom I have already mentioned. In his library there was, according to the information given me, an old collection of *daïnos*, as well as some poems in old Prussian. Having written to Count Szemioth to explain the object of my visit, I received a most courteous invitation to spend as much time at his Castle of Medintiltas as my researches might need. He ended his letter by saying very gracefully that he prided himself on speaking Jmoude almost as well as his peasants, and would be only too pleased to help me in what he described as a great and interesting undertaking. Like some of the wealthiest landowners in Lithuania, he was of the same evangelical faith of which I have the honour to be a minister. I had been warned that the Count was somewhat eccentric, though he was also very hospitable, a patron of the sciences and literature, and especially sympathetic to those who cultivated them. I accordingly set out for Medintiltas.

At the castle steps I was met by the Count's steward, who immediately led me to the rooms prepared for me.

'The Count', he said, 'is most sorry not to be able to dine with you today. He has a bad headache, a malady to which he is unfortunately prone. If you do not wish to dine in your room you can dine with the Countess's physician Dr. Froeber. Dinner will be ready in an hour; do not trouble to dress for it. If you have any orders to give, here is the bell.'

He withdrew, after a deep bow.

The room was vast, well furnished, and decorated with mirrors and gilding. On one side it looked out on to a garden, or rather the park belonging to the castle, and on the other side on to the principal courtyard. In spite of the statement that there was no need to dress, I felt obliged to get my dress coat out of my trunk, and I was in my shirt-sleeves busy unpacking my things when the sound of carriage wheels drew me to the window overlooking the courtyard. A handsome barouche had just come in. It contained a lady in black, a gentleman, and a woman dressed in Lithuanian peasant costume, but so tall and strongly built that at first I took her for a man in disguise. She stepped out first; two other women, no less robust in appearance, were already standing on the steps. The gentleman leant over towards the lady dressed in black, and, to my great surprise, unbuckled a broad leather belt which held her to her seat in the carriage. I noticed that this lady had long white hair, very much dishevelled, and that her large, wide-open eyes were staring vacantly. She looked like a waxen figure. After unfastening her, her companion spoke to her very respectfully, hat in hand; but she did not appear to pay the slightest attention to him. He then turned to the servants and made a slight sign to them with his head. Immediately the three women took hold of the lady in black, and, in spite of her efforts to cling to the carriage, lifted her out as if she were a feather and carried her into the castle. This scene was witnessed by several of the house servants, who did not appear to see anything extraordinary in it.

The gentleman who had directed the operation took out his watch, and asked how soon dinner would be ready.

'In a quarter of an hour, doctor', was the reply.

I guessed at once that this was Dr. Froeber, and that the lady in black was the Countess. From her age I concluded she was Count Szemioth's mother, and the precautions taken with her told me clearly enough that her reason was affected.

A few moments later the doctor himself came into my room.

'As the Count is indisposed', he said to me, 'I must introduce myself to you. I am Dr. Froeber, at your service, and I am delighted to make the acquaintance of a savant known to all readers of the Königsberg *Scientific and Literary Gazette*. Would it be agreeable to you if dinner were served?'

I replied to this compliment as well as I could, and told him that if it was time to go down to dinner, I was ready to accompany him.

As soon as we entered the dining-room, a major-domo offered us, in accordance with a northern custom, a silver salver laden with liqueurs and a few piquant and highly spiced dishes calculated to whet the appetite.

'Allow me, sir, speaking as a doctor, to recommend a glass of that *starka*, a true Cognac brandy casked forty years ago. It is the queen of liqueurs. Take a Drontheim anchovy; nothing is better for opening and preparing the alimentary canal, the most important organ in the body. . . . And now to table. Why do we not speak in German? You come from Königsberg, I from Memel; but I studied at Jena. We shall be more at ease like that, and the servants, who only know Polish and Russian, will not understand us.'

We ate at first in silence; then, after drinking my first glass of Madeira, I asked the doctor if the Count were often inconvenienced by the indisposition which had deprived us of his presence that evening.

'Yes and no', replied the doctor. 'It depends what outings he makes.'

'How so?'

'When he takes the Rosienie road, for instance, he comes back with a headache, and in a savage temper.'

'I have been to Rosienie myself without that happening to me.'

'That, Professor,' he replied, laughing, 'is because you are not in love.'

I sighed, thinking of Mademoiselle Gertrude Weber.

'Does the Count's fiancée live at Rosienie, then?' I asked.

'Yes, in that neighbourhood; but I cannot say whether she is engaged to him. She is a real flirt, and will drive him off his head, as has happened with his mother.'

'I gather, in fact, that the Countess is ill?'

'She is mad, my dear sir, mad! And I was even madder to come here!'

'Let us hope that your attentions will restore her to health.'

The doctor shook his head, and looked attentively at the colour of the glass of claret which he held in his hand.

'The man you see before you, Professor, was once surgeon-major in the Kalouga regiment. At Sebastopol we were cutting off arms and legs from morning till night; not to mention the shells which were coming down among us as thick as flies on a galled horse. But ill-lodged and ill-fed though I was at that time, I was not as bored as I am here, where I eat and drink of the best, am lodged like a prince, and paid like a Court physician. . . . But liberty, my dear sir! . . . Just imagine, with this she-devil I have not a moment to call my own.'

'Has she been under your care for long?'

'Less than two years; but she has been insane for at least twenty-seven, since before the birth of the Count. Did no one tell you this either at Rosienie or Kowno? Listen, then, for it is a case on which I intend to write an article some day for the *St. Petersburg Medical Journal*. She is mad from fear. . . .'

'From fear? How can that be?'

'She had a fright. She is of the house of Keystut. . . . Oh,

there are no *mésalliances* in this house. We descend from
Gedymin. . . . Well, Professor, two or three days after her
marriage, which took place in this castle where we are
dining (I drink to your health . . .), the Count, the father of
the present one, went out hunting. Our Lithuanian ladies
are regular amazons, as you know. The Countess accompanied him to the hunt. . . . She stayed behind, or got in
advance of the huntsmen—I don't know which. . . . Well, all
at once, the Count saw the Countess's little Cossack, a lad
of twelve or fourteen, come up at full gallop.

' "Master!" he said, "a bear has carried off the Countess."

' "Where?" cried the Count.

' "Over there", replied the little Cossack.

'The whole hunt dashed towards the spot he pointed out,
but there was no Countess to be seen. Her strangled horse
lay on one side, and on the other her pelisse in rags. They
searched and beat the wood in all directions. At last a
huntsman cried out: "There is the bear!" and sure enough,
the bear was crossing a clearing, still dragging the Countess,
doubtless in order to devour her undisturbed in a thicket,
for those animals are great gourmands, and they like to dine
at ease, like monks. A bridegroom of two days, the Count
was most chivalrous, and tried to fling himself upon the
bear, with his hunting knife in his hand; but, my dear sir,
a Lithuanian bear does not let himself be run through like a
stag. Fortunately the Count's gun-bearer, a low fellow, so
drunk that morning as to be unable to tell a rabbit from a
deer, fired his rifle, more than a hundred paces off, without
caring whether the bullet hit the animal or the woman.'

'And he killed the bear?'

'Stone dead. It takes a drunkard to score a hit like that.
There are also predestined bullets, Professor. We have
sorcerers here who sell them quite cheap. . . . The Countess
was badly scratched, unconscious, of course, and had one
leg broken. They carried her home, and she recovered
consciousness, but her reason had gone. They took her to
St. Petersburg for a special consultation of four doctors

K

glittering with decorations. They said that the Countess was pregnant, and that a favourable turn might be expected after her delivery. She was to be kept in the fresh air in the country, and given whey and codeine. Each physician received a hundred roubles. Nine months later the Countess gave birth to a fine, healthy boy, but where was the "favourable turn"? Where indeed?... The Countess was more frenzied than ever. The Count showed her her son. In novels that device never fails. "Kill it! kill the animal!" she yelled; and she came close to wringing his neck. Since then, there have been phases of stupid imbecility, alternating with violent madness. There is a strong suicidal tendency. We are obliged to tie her up to take her into the fresh air, and it takes three strong women to hold her. However, Professor, I ask you to note this fact, when I have tried everything on her without being able to make her obey me, I have a means of quietening her. I threaten to cut off her hair. I fancy she must have had very beautiful hair at one time. Vanity! That is the last human feeling which has remained. Is it not odd? If I could experiment on her as I chose, I might perhaps be able to cure her.'

'By what method?'

'By thrashing her. I cured in that way twenty peasant women in a village where that terrible Russian madness, "howling",[2] had broken out. One woman begins to howl, then her companion follows suit, and in three days' time the whole village is howling. I put an end to it by flogging them. (Take a little chicken, it is very tender.) The Count has never allowed me to try the experiment.'

'What! You wanted him to consent to your abominable treatment?'

'Oh, he has never really known his mother, and besides, it would be for her own good; but tell me, Professor, would you ever have thought that fear could drive someone mad?'

[2] The Russian for a woman who is possessed is a 'howler': *klikoucha*, the root of which is *klik*, clamour, howling.

'The Countess's situation was frightful. . . . To find one-self in the claws of such a savage beast!'

'Well, her son does not take after her. A year ago he was in exactly the same predicament, but, thanks to his coolness, he escaped without a scratch.'

'From the claws of a bear?'

'A she-bear, and the biggest anyone had seen for a long time. The Count tried to attack her with his hunting spear, but with one back stroke she parried the spear, seized the Count, and felled him to the ground as easily as I could upset this bottle. He cunningly feigned death. . . . The bear smelt and sniffed him, then, instead of tearing him to pieces, she gave him a lick with her tongue. He had the presence of mind not to move, and she went on her way.'

'She thought that he was dead. I have been told that those animals won't eat a dead body.'

'We must suppose so, and abstain from making a personal investigation of the question. But, talking of fear, let me tell you about something that happened at Sebastopol. Five or six of us were sitting behind the dressing-station of the famous bastion No. 5, round a pot of beer which had been brought us. The sentry cried: "A shell!" and we all threw ourselves on our stomachs. No, not all of us: a fellow called —but there's no need to give his name—a young officer who had just come to us, remained standing up, holding his glass full of beer, just when the shell burst. It blew off the head of my poor comrade Andrew Speranski, a brave lad, and broke the pot, which, fortunately, was nearly empty. When we got up after the explosion we saw our friend in the midst of the smoke, swallowing his last mouthful of beer just as if nothing had happened. We thought he was a hero. The following day I met Captain Ghedeonof who had just come out of hospital. "I dine with you fellows today", he said, "and to celebrate my return I am treating you to cham-pagne." We sat down to table. The young officer of the beer was there. He did not know about the champagne. A bottle was being uncorked near him and bang!—the cork

hit him on the temple. He gave a cry and fainted away.
Believe me, my hero had been devilishly afraid the first time,
and if he drank his beer instead of taking cover, that was
because he had lost his head and nothing was left to him
but an unconscious mechanical movement. Indeed, Professor, the human mechanism———'

'Sir,' said a servant who had just come into the room,
'Jdanova says that the Countess will not take her food.'

'Devil take her!' growled the doctor. 'I'm coming. When
I have made my she-devil eat, Professor, we might, if agreeable to you, have a game of preference or *douratchki*.'

I expressed my regret that I was unfamiliar with these
games and, when he had gone to see his patient, I went up
to my room and wrote to Mademoiselle Gertrude.

II

It was a warm night and I had left open the window overlooking the park. I did not feel ready for sleep after I had
finished my letter, so I started examining the irregular
Lithuanian verbs again, and trying to find the origins of their
different irregularities in Sanskrit. In the midst of my
absorbing labours a tree quite close to my window was
shaken violently. I heard some dead branches crack, and it
seemed to me as though some heavy animal were trying to
climb it. Still preoccupied with the bear stories which the
doctor had told me, I got up, feeling rather uneasy, and
saw, only a few feet from my window, a human head in
the foliage of the tree, lit up plainly by the light from my
lamp. The vision lasted only a second, but the singular
brilliance of the eyes which met my gaze struck me more
than I can say. Involuntarily I took a step backwards; then
I ran to the window and asked in a stern voice what the
intruder wanted. Meanwhile he was climbing down quickly,
and, seizing a thick branch between both hands, he swung
on it, dropped to the ground, and promptly disappeared. I
rang the bell; a servant came in. I told him what had just
happened.

'Sir,' he said, 'you must be mistaken.'

'I am certain of what I am saying', I replied. 'I am afraid there is a burglar in the park.'

'That is impossible, sir.'

'So it is someone from the house, is it?'

The servant opened his eyes without replying, and finally asked me if I wanted anything. I told him to shut the window, and I got into bed.

I slept soundly, without dreaming either of bears or of burglars. In the morning while I was dressing, someone knocked at my door. I opened it and found myself face to face with a very tall, handsome young man in a Bukhara dressing-gown, holding in his hand a long Turkish pipe.

'I come to beg your pardon, Professor,' he said, 'for having welcomed such a distinguished guest so badly. I am Count Szemioth.'

I hastened to say that, on the contrary, my humble thanks were due to him for his splendid hospitality, and I asked if he had recovered from his headache.

'More or less', he said. 'At all events, until the next attack', he added, with a melancholy expression. 'Are you comfortable here? You must not forget that you are among barbarians; one must not expect too much in Samogitia.'

I assured him I was most comfortable. While I was speaking to him I could not prevent myself from studying him with a curiosity which I myself found impertinent; there was something strange about his gaze which reminded me, in spite of myself, of that of the man whom I had seen up the tree the night before....

'But what likelihood', I said to myself, 'is there that Count Szemioth would climb trees by night?'

His forehead was high and well-developed, although rather narrow. His features were extremely regular, but his eyes were too close together, and I did not think that between one lachrymal glandule and the other, there was the width of an eye, as is required by the canon of the Greek sculptors. His gaze was piercing. Our eyes met several times, in spite of ourselves, and each time we both looked away with a certain embarrassment. All at once the Count burst out laughing.

'You have recognized me!' he exclaimed.

'Recognized you?'

'Yes, you caught me yesterday playing the fool.'

'Oh, Count Szemioth!'

'I had spent the whole day indisposed, shut up in my room. As I was feeling somewhat better in the evening, I went for a walk in the garden. I saw your light and yielded to an impulse of curiosity. . . . I ought to have told you who I was, and introduced myself properly, but I was in such a ridiculous situation. . . . I felt ashamed, and so I fled. . . . Will you excuse me for having disturbed you in the midst of your work?'

He said all this with a would-be playful air; but he was blushing, and was obviously embarrassed. I did my best to reassure him that I did not retain any unpleasant impression from our first meeting, and, to change the subject, I asked him if it was true that he possessed the Samogitian Catechism of Father Lawiçki.

'That may be so; but, to tell you the truth, I don't know much about my father's library. He loved old and rare books. I hardly read anything but modern works; but we will look for it, Professor. You wish us, then, to read the Gospel in Jmoudic?'

'Don't you think, Count Szemioth, that a translation of the Scriptures into the language of this country is very desirable?'

'Certainly; nevertheless, if you will permit me a small observation, I can tell you that among the people who know no other language than Jmoudic, there is not a single person who can read.'

'Perhaps so, but I ask permission of Your Excellency[3] to point out that the greatest obstacle in the way of learning to

[3] *Siatelstvo,* 'Your shining light': the title used in addressing a count.

read is the absence of books. When the Samogitian countries have a printed text they will wish to read it, and they will learn to read. This has already happened in the case of many savages—not that I wish to apply such a term to the inhabitants of this country. Furthermore,' I went on, 'is it not a deplorable thing that a language should disappear, leaving no trace behind? Prussian has been a dead language for thirty years, and the last person who knew Cornic died the other day.'

'Sad', interrupted the Count. 'Alexander von Humboldt told my father he had seen a parrot in America that was the only living thing which knew a few words of the language of a tribe now entirely wiped out by smallpox. Will you allow me to order tea to be served here?'

While we were drinking our tea, the conversation turned upon the Jmoudic tongue. The Count found fault with the way Germans printed Lithuanian, and he was right.

'Your alphabet', he said, 'does not lend itself to our language. You have neither our J, nor our L, Y, or Ë. I have a collection of *daïnos* published last year at Königsberg, and I had immense trouble understanding the words, they are so oddly printed.'

'Your Excellency is probably referring to Lessner's *daïnos*?'

'Yes. It is very vapid poetry, don't you think?'

'He might perhaps have made a better choice. I admit that, as it is, that collection has only a purely philological interest; but I believe if a careful search were made one could manage to collect some sweeter flowers among your folk-poetry.'

'Alas! I doubt it very much, in spite of all my patriotism.'

'A few weeks ago a very fine ballad was given to me at Wilno—an historical one. . . . It is a most remarkable poem. . . . May I read it to you? I have it in my wallet.'

'With the greatest pleasure.'

He buried himself in an arm-chair, after asking my permission to smoke.

'I can't understand poetry unless I smoke', he said.

'It is called *The Three Sons of Boudrys*.'

'*The Three Sons of Boudrys*?' exclaimed the Count, with a gesture of surprise.

'Yes. Boudrys, as Your Excellency knows better than I, is an historic character.'

The Count looked at me fixedly with that odd gaze of his. There was something indefinable about it, at once timid and ferocious, which produced an almost painful impression when one was not accustomed to it. I hurriedly began to read to escape it.

THE THREE SONS OF BOUDRYS

'In the courtyard of his castle old Boudrys called together his three sons—three true Lithuanians like himself.

' "My boys," he said to them, "feed your war horses, and get ready your saddles; sharpen your swords and your javelins. It is said that at Wilne war has been declared against the three corners of the world. Olgerd is going to march against Russia, and Skirghello against our neighbours, the Poles; while Keystut is going to fall upon the Teutons.[4] You are young, strong, and bold; go and fight; and may the gods of Lithuania protect you! This year I shall not go to war, but I wish to give you some advice. There are three of you, and three roads are open to you.

' "One of you must accompany Olgerd to Russia, to the banks of Lake Ilmen, under the walls of Novgorod. Ermine skins and brocaded stuffs are to be found there in plenty, and among the merchants as many roubles as there are ice-floes in the river.

' "The second must follow Keystut on his ride. May he scatter the cross-bearing rabble! Amber there is as common as sand; their cloths are without equal for sheen and colour; their priests' vestments are ornamented with rubies.

' "The third shall cross the Niemen with Skirghello. On the other side he will find base implements of tillage. But he

---

[4] The knights of the Teutonic order.

will be able to choose some good lances and strong bucklers, and he will bring back a daughter-in-law for me.

' "The women of Poland, my sons, are the most beautiful of all our captives—playful as kittens and white as cream. Under their black brows their eyes sparkle like stars. When I was young, half a century ago, I brought back from Poland a beautiful captive who became my wife. She has long been dead, but I can never look at that side of the hearth without thinking of her."

'He blessed the youths, who were already armed and in the saddle. They set out. Autumn came, then winter. . . . But they did not come back, and old Boudrys believed them to be dead.

'There came a snowstorm, and a horseman drew near, sheltering under his black *bourka*[5] a precious burden.

' "Is that a sackful of roubles from Novgorod?" asked Boudrys.

' "No, father. I have brought you a daughter-in-law from Poland."

'In the midst of the snowstorm another horseman appeared. His *bourka* was also swollen with a precious burden.

' "What is that, my boy? Yellow amber from Germany?"

' "No, father. I have brought you a daughter-in-law from Poland."

'The snow fell in squalls. A horseman advanced, hiding a precious burden under his *bourka*. . . . But before he had shown his booty, Boudrys had invited his friends to a third wedding.'

'Bravo! Professor', cried the Count; 'you pronounce Jmoudic to perfection. But who told you this pretty *daïna*?'

'A young lady whose acquaintance I had the honour to make at Wilno, at the house of Princess Katazyna Paç.'

'What is her name?'

'The *panna* Iwinska.'

[5] Felt cloak.

'Mademoiselle Ioulka!'[6] exclaimed the Count. 'The little madcap! I might have guessed. My dear Professor, you know Jmoudic and all the learned tongues; you have read all the old books; but you have let yourself be taken in by a young girl who has read nothing but novels. She has translated for you, into more or less correct Jmoudic, one of Miçkiewicz's pretty ballads, which you have not read because it is no older than I am. If you wish, I will show it to you in Polish, or, if you prefer, in an excellent Russian translation by Pushkin.'

I confess I was quite dumbfounded. How the Dorpat professor would have laughed if I had published as an original the *daïna* of the sons of Boudrys!

Instead of deriving amusement from my embarrassment, the Count, with exquisite politeness, hastened to change the conversation.

'So you have met Mademoiselle Ioulka?' he said.

'I have had the honour of being presented to her.'

'What do you think of her? Speak quite frankly.'

'She is a most charming young lady.'

'So you are pleased to say.'

'She is exceedingly pretty.'

'Oh!'

'What! Don't you think she has the loveliest eyes in the world?'

'Yes . . .'

'A complexion of the most extraordinary whiteness? . . . I remember a Persian *ghazel*, in which a lover extols the fineness of his mistress's skin. "When she drinks red wine", he said, "you see it pass down her throat." The *panna* Iwinska made me think of that Persian poem.'

'Mademoiselle Ioulka may possibly embody that phenomenon; but I am not so sure that she has any blood in her veins. . . . She has no heart. . . . She is as white and cold as snow!'

He rose and walked round the room for some time without

6 Julienne.

speaking, as if to hide his emotion; then, stopping suddenly——

'Forgive me,' he said, 'we were talking, I believe, about folk-poetry. . . .'

'We were, Your Excellency.'

'After all it must be admitted that she translated Mickie-wicz very prettily. . . . "Playful as a kitten, . . . white as cream, . . . eyes like stars". . . . That is a portrait of herself, don't you agree?'

'Absolutely, Your Excellency.'

'As for this roguish trick . . . a very ill-judged one, to be sure. . . . The poor child is bored to death living with an old aunt. She leads the life of a nun.'

'At Wilno she went into society. I saw her at a ball given by the officers of the —— regiment.'

'Ah, yes, the society of young officers must suit her ad-mirably! Laughing with one, gossiping with another, and flirting with all of them. . . . Will you come and see my father's library, Professor?'

I followed him to a long gallery, lined with a great many handsomely bound books which, to judge from the dust that covered their edges, were rarely opened. Imagine my delight at finding that one of the first volumes I pulled out of a glass case was the *Catechismus Samogiticus!* I could not help uttering a cry of pleasure. Some sort of mysterious attraction must exert its influence unknown to us. . . . The Count took the book and, after turning over the leaves care-lessly, wrote on the fly-leaf: *To Professor Wittembach, from Michael Szemioth.* I cannot say how grateful I was, and I made a mental resolution that after my death this precious book should grace my own University library.

'Please consider this library as your study', the Count said to me; 'you shall never be disturbed here.'

III

After breakfast the following day the Count suggested that I should take a walk with him. The object was to visit the *kapas* (the name given by the Lithuanians to the tumuli which the Russians call *kourgâne*), which was very famous locally, because in former times poets and magicians (they were one and the same thing) gathered there on certain solemn occasions.

'I have a very quiet horse to offer you', he said. 'I regret that I cannot take you by carriage, but the fact is that the road we are going to take is not fit for carriages.'

I would rather have stayed in the library taking notes, but I felt I should not express any wish contrary to that of my generous host, and I accepted. The horses were waiting for us at the foot of the steps; in the courtyard a groom held a dog in leash.

'Do you know much about dogs, Professor?' asked the Count, stopping for a moment and turning to me.

'Hardly anything, Your Excellency.'

'The Staroste of Zorany, where I have some property, has sent me this spaniel, which he praises highly. Allow me to show him to you.' He called to the groom, who came up with the dog. He was indeed a splendid creature. The dog, already used to the man, leapt about joyfully and seemed full of life; but when within a few yards of the Count, he put his tail between his legs, started back, and seemed struck with sudden terror. The Count patted him, and at this the dog set up a dismal howl.

'I think he will turn out a good dog. Look after him well', he said, after examining him for some time with the eye of a connoisseur. Then he mounted his horse.

'Professor,' he said, as soon as we were in the avenue leading to the castle, 'you have just seen that dog's fear. I wanted you to see it for yourself. In your capacity as a savant, you must explain enigmas. . . . Why should animals be afraid of me?'

'Really, Your Excellency does me the honour of taking me for an Oedipus, while I am only a humble professor of comparative philology. It might be . . .'

'Observe', he broke in, 'that I never beat either horses or

dogs. I would have scruples about whipping a poor beast who makes a mistake without knowing it. All the same, you can hardly conceive the aversion I inspire in dogs and horses. It takes me twice the time and trouble to accustom them to me that it would anyone else. It took me a long time before I could break in the horse you are riding, but now he is as quiet as a lamb.'

'I believe, Your Excellency, that animals are physiognomists, and can tell at once if people whom they are seeing for the first time like them or not. I suspect that you only like animals for the services they render you; on the other hand, some people have an instinctive partiality for certain animals, and they notice that straight away. Now I, for instance, have always had an instinctive liking for cats. They rarely run away from me when I try to stroke them, and I have never been scratched by a cat.'

'That is quite likely', said the Count; 'I cannot say I have any real affection for animals. . . . They are scarcely any better than human beings. . . . We are now coming into a forest, Professor, where the kingdom of the beasts still flourishes—the *matecznik*, the great womb, the great nursery of the animals. Yes, according to our national traditions, no one has yet penetrated its depths, no one has been able to reach the heart of these woods and marshes, except, of course, the poets and magicians, who penetrate everywhere. Here the animals all live as in a republic . . . or under a constitutional government, I cannot tell which of the two. Lions, bears, elks, *joubrs*, our wild oxen or aurochs, all live very happily together. The mammoth, which is still extant here, is very highly thought of; he is, I believe, the Marshal of the Diet. They have a very strict police force, and if they decide that any beast is vicious they sentence him to exile. Then it is a case of out of the frying-pan into the fire; the animal is obliged to venture into the land of men, and few escape.'[7]

[7] See *Messire Thaddée*, by Miçkiewicz, and *La Pologne Captive*, by M. Charles Edmond.

'A very curious legend,' I exclaimed, 'but, Your Excellency, you speak of the aurochs, that noble animal which Caesar has described in his *Commentaries,* and which the Merovingian kings hunted in the forest of Compiègne. I have heard that they still exist in Lithuania—is that really so?'

'Certainly. My father himself killed a *joubr*, having obtained permission from the Government, of course. You can see the head in the large dining-hall. I myself have never seen one. I believe they are very rare. On the other hand, we have wolves and bears here in abundance. It is in case of a possible encounter with one of those fellows that I have brought this instrument' (and he produced a Circassian *tchekhole*[8] which he carried slung across his back), 'and my groom has a double-barrelled rifle at his saddle-bow.'

We were beginning to penetrate into the forest. Soon the narrow track that we were following disappeared altogether. Every few moments we were obliged to ride round enormous trees whose low branches barred our way. Some of them, which had died of old age and fallen over, looked like bulwarks crowned with a line of wire entanglements impossible to scale. Elsewhere we encountered deep pools covered with water-lilies and duckweed. Farther on we came to clearings where the grass shone like emeralds; but woe to anyone who ventured on to it, for this rich and deceptive vegetation usually hides abysses of mud into which both horse and rider would disappear for ever. . . . The difficulties of the route had interrupted our conversation. All my attention was devoted to following the Count, and I admired the imperturbable sureness with which he found his way without a compass, and always hit upon the right direction which had to be taken to reach the *kapas*. It was obvious that he had frequently hunted in these wild forests.

At last we perceived the tumulus in the centre of a large clearing. It was very high and surrounded by a moat still clearly recognizable in spite of the undergrowth and the

[8] A Circassian gun-case.

landslips. It seems that it had already been excavated. At the summit I noticed the remains of an erection built of stones, some of which bore traces of fire. A substantial quantity of ashes, mixed with pieces of charcoal, with here and there fragments of coarse crockery, showed that there had been a fire on the top of the tumulus for a considerable time. According to popular tradition, human sacrifices used to be offered up in the *kapases*; but there is hardly any extinct religion to which these abominable rites have not been attributed, and I doubt if there is any historical evidence to justify a similar theory with regard to the ancient Lithuanians.

We were coming down from the tumulus to rejoin our horses, which we had left on the far side of the moat, when we saw an old woman approaching us, leaning on a stick and holding a basket in her hand.

'Kind gentlemen,' she said to us as she came up, 'I beg you for alms for the love of God. Give me something for a glass of brandy to warm my poor body.'

The Count threw her a coin, and asked what she was doing in the wood, so far from any habitation. Her only answer was to show him her basket, which was full of mushrooms. Although my knowledge of botany was very limited, it seemed to me that several of the mushrooms belonged to poisonous species.

'My good woman,' I said, 'you aren't going to eat those, I hope.'

'Sir,' the old woman replied, with a sad smile, 'poor folk eat everything the good God gives them.'

'You are not acquainted with our Lithuanian stomachs', the Count broke in; 'they are lined with sheet iron. Our peasants eat every kind of mushroom they find, and are none the worse for that.'

'At least prevent her from trying the *agaricus necator* she has in her basket', I cried, and I stretched out my hand to take one of the most poisonous of the mushrooms, but the old woman quickly withdrew the basket.

'Take care', she said in a frightened tone; 'they are protected. . . . *Pirkuns! Pirkuns!*'

Pirkuns, I should explain in passing, is the Samogitian name for the divinity the Russians call *Pyerun*; it is the Jupiter *tonans* of the Slavs. If I was surprised when I heard the old woman invoke a pagan god, I was much more astonished to see the mushrooms rise up. The black head of a snake lifted itself at least a foot out of the basket. I jumped back, and the Count spat over his shoulder in accordance with the superstitious custom of the Slavs, who believe that in this way they turn away misfortune, as did the ancient Romans. The old woman put the basket on the ground, and crouched down beside it; then she held out her hand towards the snake, pronouncing some unintelligible words which sounded like an incantation. The snake remained motionless for a moment; then it curled itself round the shrivelled arm of the old woman and disappeared up the sleeve of her sheepskin cloak which, with a dirty chemise, comprised, I believe, the whole costume of this Lithuanian Circe. The old woman looked at us with a little laugh of triumph, like a conjurer who has just performed a difficult trick. Her face wore that mixture of cunning and stupidity which is often noticeable in so-called witches, who for the most part are at once scoundrels and dupes.

'Here', said the Count in German, 'you have an example of local colour; a witch who charms a snake, at the foot of a *kapas*, in the presence of a learned professor and an ignorant Lithuanian nobleman. It would make a capital subject for a genre picture by your fellow countryman Knauss. . . . If you wish to have your fortune told, this is a good opportunity.'

I replied that I had no desire to encourage such practices.

'I would much rather', I added, 'ask her if she knows anything about that curious tradition of which you spoke. Good woman,' I said to her, 'have you heard tell of a part of this forest where the animals live in a community, independent of man's rule?'

The old woman nodded her head and gave a low laugh, half silly, half cunning.

'I have just come from it', she said. 'The beasts have lost their king. Noble, the lion, is dead; the animals are about to elect another king. If you go there perhaps they will make you king.'

'What are you saying, mother?' cried the Count, roaring with laughter. 'Do you know to whom you are talking? Don't you know that this gentleman is . . . (what the devil do they call a professor in Jmoude?) a great savant, a sage, a *waïdelote*?'[9]

The witch gazed at him fixedly.

'I was mistaken', she said. 'It is you who must go there. You will be their king, not he; you are tall and strong, and you have claws and teeth.'

'What do you think of the epigrams she keeps shooting at us?' the Count asked me. 'Can you show us the way, mother?' he said to her.

She pointed with her hand to a part of the forest.

'Indeed?' said the Count. 'And how do you get across the marsh? I ought to explain, Professor, that where she pointed there is an impassable swamp, a lake of liquid mud covered with green grass. Last year a stag that I wounded plunged into that marsh, and I saw him sink slowly, slowly. . . . After five minutes I could see nothing but his antlers, and soon he disappeared completely, two of my dogs with him.'

'But I am not heavy', said the old woman, chuckling. 'I think you find it easy to cross the marsh, on a broomstick.'

A flash of anger shone in the old woman's eyes.

'Sir,' she said, returning to the drawling and nasal tone of the beggar, 'haven't you a pipe of tobacco to give a poor woman? You would do better to search for a way across the swamp than to go to Dowghielly', she added in a lower voice.

---

[9] A bad translation of the word 'Professor'. The *waïdelotes* were Lithuanian bards.

'Dowghielly!' cried the Count, blushing. 'What do you mean?'

I could not help noticing that this word produced a strange effect upon him. He was visibly embarrassed: he lowered his head in order to hide his confusion, and busied himself opening the tobacco pouch which hung from the hilt of his hunting-knife.

'No, don't go to Dowghielly', repeated the old woman. 'The little white dove is not for you, is she, *Pirkuns*?'

At that moment the snake's head appeared out of the collar of the old woman's cloak and stretched up to its mistress's ear. The reptile, doubtless trained to perform this trick, moved its jaws as if it were speaking.

'He says I am right', said the old woman.

The Count gave her a handful of tobacco.

'Do you know me?' he asked her.

'No, sir.'

'I am the master of Medintiltas. Come and see me one of these days; I will give you some tobacco and brandy.'

The old woman kissed his hand and hurried away. A moment later we had lost sight of her. The Count remained thoughtful, tying and untying the strings of his pouch, hardly conscious of what he was doing.

'Professor,' he said to me after a fairly long silence, 'you are going to laugh at me. That old crone knows both me and the road which she showed me, better than she pretended. . . . After all, there is nothing so very surprising in that. I am as well known in this part of the world as the white wolf. The jade has seen me several times on the road to Dow- ghielly Castle. . . . A marriageable young lady lives there, so she concluded that I was in love with her. . . . Then some handsome fellow must have bribed her to threaten me with bad luck. . . . That is obvious. All the same . . . in spite of myself, her words have affected me. I am almost frightened by them. . . . You laugh, and you have good cause to laugh. . . . The truth is that I had planned to go and ask for dinner at the Castle of Dowghielly, and now I hesitate. . . . I am a great fool. Come, Professor, you decide the matter. Shall we go?'

'In questions of marriage I never give advice', I said laughingly. 'I shall take good care not to express an opinion.'

We had come back to our horses.

'The horse shall choose for us', cried the Count as he vaulted into the saddle and let the bridle lie slack.

The horse did not hesitate; he immediately took a little path, which, after several turnings, ran into a metalled road which led to Dowghielly. Half an hour later we reached the castle steps.

At the sound of our horses a pretty fair head appeared at a window, framed between two curtains. I recognized the perfidious translator of Mięckiewicz.

'Welcome!' she said. 'You could not have come at a better time, Count Szemioth. A dress from Paris has just arrived for me. You won't recognize me, I shall look so beautiful.'

The curtains closed again.

'It's certainly not for me that she's putting on this dress for the first time', the Count muttered between his teeth while mounting the steps.

He introduced me to Madame Dowghiello, the aunt of the *panna* Iwinksa, who received me graciously and spoke to me of my latest articles in the Königsberg *Scientific and Literary Gazette*.

'The Professor has come to complain to you', said the Count, 'of a malicious trick which Mademoiselle Julienne has played on him.'

'She is a child, Professor; you must forgive her. She often drives me to distraction with her follies. I had more sense at sixteen than she has at twenty, but she is a good girl at heart, and she has many good qualities. She is an admirable musician, she paints flowers exquisitely, and she speaks French, German, and Italian equally well. . . . She embroiders . . .'

'And she composes Jmoudic verses', added the Count with a laugh.

'She is incapable of that', exclaimed Madame Dowghiello; and they had to explain her niece's prank.

Madame Dowghiello was well educated, and knew the antiquities of her country. Her conversation was particularly agreeable to me. She read a good many of our German reviews, and held very sane opinions on philology. I admit that I did not notice how long Mademoiselle Iwinska took to dress, but it seemed a long time to Count Szemioth, who got up and sat down again, looked out of the window, and drummed on the panes with his fingers like a man who is running out of patience.

At last, after three-quarters of an hour, Mademoiselle Julienne appeared, wearing with grace and pride a dress which would require more critical knowledge than mine to describe. She was followed by her French governess.

'Don't I look pretty?' she said to the Count, turning round slowly so that he could see her from all sides.

She did not look either at the Count or at me, but at her dress.

'Ioulka,' said Madame Dowghiello, 'why don't you say good day to the Professor? He is complaining about you.'

'Ah, Professor!' she cried, with a charming little pout. 'What have I done? Are you going to make me do penance?'

'We should be punishing ourselves, Mademoiselle, if we deprived ourselves of your presence', I answered. 'I am far from complaining; on the contrary, I congratulate myself on having learnt, thanks to you, that the Lithuanian Muse has reappeared more brilliant than ever.'

She lowered her head, and, putting her hands before her face, taking care not to disarrange her hair, she said, in the tones of a child who has just stolen some sweets:

'Forgive me; I will not do it again.'

'I will only pardon you, my dear Pani,' I said to her, 'if you will fulfil a certain promise which you were good enough to make to me at Wilmo, at the house of the Princess Katazyna Paç.'

'What promise?' she asked, raising her head and laughing.

'Have you forgotten so soon? You promised me that if we met in Samogitia, you would let me see a certain country dance which you said was enchanting.'

'Oh, the russalka! I am delightful in it; and the very man I need is here.'

She ran to a table loaded with music-books and, looking through one hastily, put it on the piano stand.

'Here, my dear, *allegro presto*', she said, addressing her governess. And she played the prelude herself, without sitting down, to show the time.

'Come here, Count Michael! You are too much of a Lithuanian not to be able to dance the russalka; ... but dance like a peasant, you understand.'

Madame Dowghiello tried in vain to object. The Count and I insisted. He had his reasons, for his part in the dance was extremely agreeable, as you will soon see. The governess, after a few attempts, said she thought she could play that kind of waltz, strange though it was; so Mademoiselle Iwinska, after moving some chairs and a table that were in the way, took her partner by the collar of his coat and led him into the centre of the room.

'I must explain to you, Professor, that I am a russalka, at your service.'

She made a low bow.

'A russalka is a water nymph. There is one in each of the pools of black water which adorn our forests. Never go near them! The russalka comes out, even lovelier than I, if that is possible; she drags you down to the bottom, where in all probability she gobbles you up. . . .'

'A real siren', I cried.

'He', continued Mademoiselle Iwinska, pointing to Count Szemioth, 'is a very foolish young fisherman who exposes himself to my clutches, and, to make the pleasure last longer, I fascinate him by dancing round him for a time. . . . But, to do it properly I need a sarafane.[10] What a pity! You must please excuse this dress, which has neither character nor

[10] A peasant's skirt without a bodice.

local colour. . . . Oh! and I am wearing shoes! It is quite impossible to dance the russalka with shoes on . . . and shoes with high heels too!'

She pulled up her dress, and, daintily shaking a pretty little foot, at the risk of showing her leg, she sent the shoe flying to the end of the drawing-room. The other followed the first, and she stood there on the floor in her silk stockings.

'We are quite ready', she said to the governess.

And the dance began.

The russalka dances round and round her partner; he stretches out his arms to seize her, but she slips underneath them and escapes. It is very graceful, and the music has movement and originality. The figure ends when the partner tries to seize the russalka to give her a kiss, and she makes a bound, strikes him on the shoulder, and he falls dead at her feet. . . . But the Count improvised a variation, which was to clasp the mischievous creature in his arms and kiss her again and again. Mademoiselle Iwinska uttered a little cry, blushed deeply, and threw herself, pouting, on to a couch, complaining that he had hugged her like the bear that he was. I saw that the comparison did not please the Count, for it reminded him of the family misfortune, and his brow darkened. For my part, I thanked Mademoiselle Iwinska warmly, and praised her dance, which seemed to me to have a thoroughly antique flavour, and recalled the sacred dances of the Greeks. I was interrupted by a servant announcing General and Princess Veliaminof. Mademoiselle Iwinska leapt from the sofa to retrieve her shoes, hastily thrust in her little feet, and ran to meet the Princess, making two profound curtsies one after the other. I noticed that at each curtsy she adroitly drew on part of one shoe. The General had brought with him two aides-de-camp and, like us, had come to ask for pot-luck. In any other country I imagine the mistress of the house would have been a little embarrassed at receiving all at once six hungry and unexpected guests; but Lithuanian hospitality is so lavish that the dinner was not more than half an hour late, I think; there were too many hot and cold pies, however.

IV

The dinner was very lively. The General gave us a very interesting account of the dialects spoken in the Caucasus, some of which are Aryan and the others Turanian, although between the different peoples there is a remarkable uniformity in manners and customs. I myself was obliged to talk of my travels because Count Szemioth congratulated me on the way I sat a horse, and said he had never met a minister or a professor who could have managed so easily such a journey as the one we had made. I had to explain to him that, commissioned by the Bible Society to write a work on the language of the *Charruas*, I had spent three and a half years in the Republic of Uruguay, nearly always on horseback, and living in the pampas among the Indians. This led me to relate how, after I had been lost for three days in those boundless plains, without food or water, I had been reduced, like the *gauchos* who accompanied me, to bleed my horse and drink his blood.

All the ladies uttered a cry of horror. The General observed that the Kalmuks did the same in similar extremities. The Count asked me what the drink had tasted like.

'Morally, it was most repugnant', I replied, 'but physically, I found it very stimulating, and it is owing to it that I have the honour of dining here today. Many Europeans, I mean white men, who have lived for a long time with the Indians, become accustomed to it and even acquire a taste for it. My good friend Don Fructuoso Rivero, the President of the Republic, hardly ever missed a chance of gratifying that taste. I remember that one day, when he was going to Congress in full uniform, he passed a *rancho* where a young foal was being bled. He got off his horse to ask for a *chupon*, a suck; after which he delivered one of his most eloquent speeches.'

'Your President is a hideous monster', cried Mademoiselle Iwinska.

'Pardon me, my dear Pani,' I said to her, 'he is a very distinguished person, with a fine enlightened mind. He speaks to perfection several Indian dialects which are very difficult, especially *Charrua*, because of its verbs which take innumerable forms, according to whether their object is direct or indirect, and even according to the social relations of the persons who speak.'

I was about to give some very curious instances of the construction of the *Charrua* verb, but the Count interrupted me to ask what part of the horse they bled when they wanted to drink its blood.

'For goodness' sake, my dear Professor,' cried Mademoiselle Iwinska, with a comic expression of terror, 'don't tell him. He is quite capable of killing his whole stable, and then eating us up ourselves when he has no more horses left.'

Upon this sally the ladies laughingly left the table to prepare tea and coffee while we smoked. In a quarter of an hour they sent from the drawing-room for the General. We all prepared to go with him; but we were told that the ladies only wished one man at a time. Soon we heard loud bursts of laughter and clapping of hands coming from the drawing-room.

'Mademoiselle Ioulka is up to her pranks', said the Count.

He was sent for next; and there was more laughter and applause. It was my turn after this. By the time I had reached the room every face had taken on a pretended gravity which did not bode well. I expected some trick.

'Professor,' said the General to me in his most official manner, 'these ladies maintain that we have given too kind a reception to their champagne, and they will not admit us to their company until after a test. You must walk from the middle of the room to that wall with your eyes bandaged, and touch it with your finger. You see how easy it is; you have only to walk straight. Are you able to keep a straight line?'

'I think so, General.'

Mademoiselle Iwinska then threw a handkerchief over my eyes and tied it tightly behind.

'You are in the middle of the room', she said; 'stretch out your hand. . . That's right! I wager that you won't touch the wall.'

'Forward, march!' called out the General.

There were only five or six steps to take. I advanced very slowly, sure that I should encounter some cord or footstool treacherously placed in my path to trip me up, and I could hear stifled laughter which increased my confusion. At last I believed I was quite close to the wall, when my outstretched finger suddenly plunged into something cold and sticky. I made a grimace and started backwards, which set the on-lookers laughing. I tore off my bandage, and saw Mademoiselle Iwinska standing near me holding a pot of honey, into which I had thrust my finger, thinking that I was touching the wall. My only consolation was to see the two aides-de-camp pass through the same ordeal, with no better result than I.

For the rest of the evening Mademoiselle Iwinska never ceased to give vent to her whimsical humour. Ever teasing, ever mischievous, she made first one, then another, the butt of her fun. I observed, however, that she addressed herself most frequently to the Count, who, I must say, never took offence, and even seemed to enjoy her teasing. But when, on the other hand, she started on one of the aides-de-camp, he frowned, and I saw his eyes kindle with that dull fire which was really rather terrifying. 'Playful as a kitten and as white as cream.' It seemed to me that in writing that verse Miçkie-wicz had wished to draw the portrait of the *panna* Iwinska.

V

It was quite late before we retired to bed. In many of the great houses in Lithuania there is plenty of splendid silver plate, fine furniture, and valuable Persian carpets; but there are no comfortable feather beds, as in our dear Germany, to offer the tired guest. Rich or poor, nobleman or peasant, a Slav can sleep quite soundly on a board. The Castle of Dowghielly was no exception to this general rule. In the room to which the Count and I were conducted there were only two couches covered with morocco leather. This did not disturb me as I had often slept on the bare earth during my travels, and I laughed a little at the Count's exclamations at his compatriots' lack of civilization. A servant came to take off our boots and gave us dressing-gowns and slippers. When the Count had taken off his coat, he walked up and down for a while in silence; then he stopped in front of the couch on which I had already stretched myself out.

'What do you think of Ioulka?' he asked me.

'I think she is charming.'

'Yes, but such a flirt! . . . Do you believe she really likes that little fair-haired captain?'

'The aide-de-camp? . . . How should I know?'

'He's a fop! . . . So women are bound to like him.'

'I deny your conclusion, Count. Do you wish me to tell you the truth? Mademoiselle Iwinska is much more eager to please Count Szemioth than to please all the aides-de-camp in the army.'

He blushed without replying; but it seemed to me that my words had given him great pleasure. He walked up and down again for some time without speaking; then, looking at his watch, he said:

'Good gracious, we would do well to go to sleep; it's late.'

He took his rifle and his hunting-knife, which had been placed in our room, put them in a cupboard, and took the key out of the lock.

'Will you keep it?' he said; and to my great surprise he gave it to me. 'I might forget it. You are sure to have a better memory than I have.'

'The best way not to forget your weapons would be to place them on that table near your sofa', I said.

'No. . . . Look here, to tell you the truth, I don't like to have arms by me when I am asleep. . . . This is the reason.

When I was in the Grodno Hussars, I slept one night in a room with a comrade, and my pistols were on a chair beside me. In the night I was awakened by a report. I had a pistol in my hand; I had fired it, and the bullet had passed within two inches of my comrade's head. . . . I have never been able to remember the dream I had had.'

I was a little disturbed by this anecdote. I was safe from having a bullet through my head; but, when I looked at my companion's tall figure, his Herculean shoulders, and his muscular arms covered with black down, I could not help recognizing that he was perfectly able to strangle me with his hands if he had a bad dream. I took care, however, not to show the slightest uneasiness; only I put a light on a chair beside my couch, and began to read Lawiçki's *Catechism*, which I had brought with me. The Count wished me good night, and lay down on his sofa, on which he turned over five or six times; at last he appeared to fall asleep, although he was doubled up like Horace's lover who, shut up in a chest, had his head touching his bent knees:

> . . . Turpi clausus in arca,
> Contractum genibus tangas caput. . . .

From time to time he sighed heavily, or gave a kind of rattling breath, which I attributed to the peculiar position in which he had chosen to sleep. An hour perhaps passed in this way, and I myself became drowsy. I shut my book, and I was settling myself as comfortably as was possible on my bed, when an odd chuckling sound from my neighbour gave me a start. I looked at the Count. His eyes were shut; his whole body was trembling; and from his half-opened lips there escaped some hardly articulate words.

'So fresh! . . . So white! . . . The Professor doesn't know what he's talking about. . . . Horse is not worth a straw. . . . What a delicious morsel!'

Then he began to bite with all his might the cushion on which his head was resting, growling at the same time so loudly that he woke himself.

For my part, I remained quite still on my couch, and pretended to be asleep. Nevertheless, I watched him. He sat up, rubbed his eyes, sighed sadly, and remained for nearly an hour without changing his position, apparently absorbed in his reflections. I was, however, very ill at ease, and I inwardly vowed never again to sleep beside the Count. But in the long run weariness overcame uneasiness, and when the servant came to our room in the morning, we were both sleeping soundly.

VI

We returned to Medintiltas after breakfast. When I found Dr. Froeber alone, I told him that I believed the Count was unwell, that he had terrible dreams, that he was possibly a somnambulist, and that he could be dangerous in that condition.

'I am aware of all that', said the doctor.

'With an athletic constitution he is at the same time as highly strung as a pretty woman. Perhaps he gets that from his mother. . . . She has been devilishly bad today. . . . I don't believe much in those stories of the fears and longings of pregnant women; but what is certain is that the Countess is mad, and madness can be inherited. . . .'

'But the Count', I replied, 'is perfectly sane: he has a sound judgement; he is much better educated than, I admit, I would have expected; he loves reading. . . .'

'I grant that, my dear sir, I grant that; but he often behaves strangely. Sometimes he shuts himself up for several days; often he roams about at night. He reads unheard-of books . . . about German metaphysics, physiology, and heaven knows what else. Why only yesterday a whole crate of them came from Leipzig. Must I speak plainly? A Hercules needs a Hebe. There are some very pretty peasant girls here. . . . On Saturday evenings, when they have washed, you might mistake them for princesses. . . . There isn't one of them but would be proud to distract my lord. I, at his age, the devil take me! . . . No, he has no mistress;

he will not marry; he is wrong. He ought to have something to give him relief.'

The doctor's coarse materialism shocked me deeply, and I abruptly terminated the conversation by saying that I sincerely hoped that Count Szemioth would find a wife worthy of him. I had been surprised, I must admit, to learn from the doctor of the Count's taste for philosophical studies. It went against all my preconceived ideas that this officer of the Hussars, this ardent sportsman, should read about German metaphysics and take an interest in physiology. The doctor spoke the truth, however, as I discovered that very day.

'How do you explain, Professor,' the Count asked me suddenly towards the close of dinner, 'how do you explain the *duality* or the *duplicity* of our nature?'

And when he observed that I did not quite follow him, he went on:

'Have you never found yourself at the top of a tower, or even at the edge of a precipice, experiencing at the same time a desire to throw yourself into space, and an absolutely contrary feeling of terror?'

'That can be explained on purely physical grounds', said the doctor; 'first, the fatigue of walking uphill sends a rush of blood to the brain, which . . .'

'Let us leave blood out of it, doctor,' broke in the Count impatiently, 'and take another instance. You are holding a loaded firearm. Your best friend is there. The idea occurs to you to put a ball through his head. You hold murder in the greatest horror, but all the same you think of committing it. I believe, gentlemen, that if all the thoughts which come into our heads in the course of an hour . . . I believe that if all *your* thoughts, Professor, whom I hold to be so wise, were written down, they would form a folio volume perhaps, after the perusal of which there would not be a single lawyer who could fail to have you deprived of control of your estate, nor a judge who would not put you in prison or else in a lunatic asylum.'

'That judge, Count, would certainly not condemn me for having hunted, for more than an hour this morning, for the mysterious law which decides that Slavonic verbs take a future tense when combined with a preposition; but if by chance I had had some other thought, what conclusion could you draw from that against me? I am no more master of my thoughts than of the external accidents which suggest them to me. Because a thought springs up in my mind, that does not mean that I have begun to put it into execution, or even resolved to do so. I have never thought of killing anybody; but, if the thought of murder comes into my mind, isn't my reason there to drive it out?'

'You talk very confidently of your reason; but is it always with us, as you say, to guide us? For reason to speak and be obeyed we need reflection, that is to say, time and sang froid. Have we always both of these? In battle I see a ricocheting bullet coming towards me; I get out of the way and thus expose my friend, for whom I would have given my life if I had had time to think. . . .'

I spoke to him of our duty as men and Christians, the obligation we are under to imitate the warrior of the Scriptures, always ready for battle; finally, I pointed out that in constantly struggling against our passions we gain fresh strength to weaken and overcome them. I only succeeded I fear, in reducing him to silence, and he did not seem convinced.

I stayed about ten days more at the castle. I paid one more visit to Dowghielly, but we did not sleep there. As on the first occasion, Mademoiselle Iwinska behaved like a mischievous spoilt child. She exercised a kind of fascination over the Count, and I did not doubt that he was very much in love with her. At the same time he knew her faults thoroughly, and was under no illusions. He knew that she was a frivolous coquette, and indifferent to anything that did not afford her amusement. I often noticed that he suffered inwardly at seeing her so petty-minded; but as soon as she paid him some little attention his face lit up, and he beamed with joy, forgetting everything else. He wished to take me to Dowghielly for a last visit the day before my departure, possibly because I used to stay talking with the aunt while he went for a stroll in the garden with the niece; but I had so much work to do that I was obliged to excuse myself, however much he insisted. He returned for dinner, although he had told us not to wait for him. He sat down at table, but could not eat. He was gloomy and ill-tempered all through the meal. From time to time his eyebrows contracted and his eyes assumed a sinister expression. When the doctor left to go to see the Countess, the Count followed me to my room and told me all that was on his mind.

'I thoroughly regret', he exclaimed, 'having left you to go and see that little ninny who makes fun of me and only cares for new faces; but, fortunately, all is over between us; I am utterly disgusted with her, and I will never see her again. . . .'

For some time he paced up and down according to his usual habit.

'You thought, perhaps, that I was in love with her?' he went on. 'That is what that fool of a doctor thinks. No, I have never loved her. Her high spirits amused me. Her white skin was a pleasure to look at. . . . That is all there is that is pleasing about her . . . her skin especially. She has no brains at all. I have never seen anything in her but just a pretty doll, agreeable to look at when one is bored and hasn't a new book. . . . Admittedly she can be described as a beauty. . . . Her skin is marvellous! . . . The blood under that skin ought to be better than a horse's. . . . Don't you think so, Professor?'

He burst out laughing, but his laughter was not a pleasant thing to hear.

I took leave of him the next day, to continue my explorations in the north of the Palatinate.

VII

They lasted about two months, and I can say that there is hardly a village in Samogitia where I have not stopped and collected a few documents. I may here be allowed, perhaps, to take this opportunity of thanking the inhabitants of that province, and especially the ecclesiastics, for the truly warm co-operation they accorded me in my research, and the excellent contributions with which they have enriched my dictionary.

After staying a week at Szawle, I was planning to embark at Klaypeda (the port which we call Memel) to return home, when I received the following letter from Count Szemioth, which was brought by one of his huntsmen:

My dear Professor, —Allow me to write to you in German for I should make even more grammatical errors if I wrote in Jmoudic, and you would lose all respect for me. I am not sure that you have much as it is, and the news that I am about to give you will probably not increase it. Without more ado, I am going to be married, and you will guess to whom. *Jove laughs at lovers vows*. So does *Pirkuns*, our Samogitian Jupiter. It is, then Mademoiselle Julienne Iwinska that I am to marry on the 8th of next month. You would be the kindest of men if you would come and attend the ceremony. All the peasantry of Medintiltas and the neighbouring districts will come to devour a few oxen and countless swine, and, when they are drunk, they will dance in the meadow which, you will remember, lies on the right of the avenue. You will see costumes and customs worthy of your attention. It will give me and also Julienne the greatest pleasure if you come, and I must add that your refusal would place us in a most awkward situation. You know that I belong to the Evangelical Communion, as does my betrothed; now, our minister who lives about thirty leagues away, is crippled with gout, and ventured to hope you would be so good as to act in his stead.

Believe me, my dear Professor,

Yours sincerely,

MICHAEL SZEMIOTH.

There was a postscript, in Jmoudic, in a pretty feminine hand.

I, the muse of Lithuania, write in Jmoudic. Michael is very impertinent to question your approval. There is no one but I indeed, who would be so silly as to marry such a fellow as him. You will see, Professor, on the 8th of next month, a bride who may be called *chic*. That is not a Jmoudic word, it is French. But please do not allow your thoughts to wander during the ceremony.

Neither the letter nor the postscript pleased me. I thought the engaged couple showed an inexcusable levity concerning such a solemn occasion. However, how was I to decline? I must admit, too, that the promised pageant had its attractions for me. In all probability, among the great number of noblemen who would be gathered together at the Castle of Medintiltas, I would not fail to find some knowledgeable people who would furnish me with useful information. My Jmoudic glossary was very good; but the meaning of a certain number of words, which I had learnt from the lips of humble peasants, was still, relatively speaking, somewhat obscure to me. All these considerations combined were sufficiently powerful to make me consent to the Count's request, and I replied that I would arrive at Medintiltas on the morning of the 8th.

How greatly I was to regret my decision!

VIII

On entering the avenue which led to the castle I saw a great number of ladies and gentlemen in morning dress standing in groups on the steps of the entrance or walking about the paths of the park. The courtyard was full of peasants in their Sunday best. The castle had a festive air; everywhere there were flowers and garlands, flags and festoons. The steward led me to the room on the ground floor which had been assigned to me, apologizing for not being able to offer me a better one; but there were so many visitors in the castle that it had been impossible to keep for me the room I had occupied during my first visit, which had been given to the wife of the Marshal of the Nobility. My new room was, however, very pleasant; it looked out on the park, and was below the Count's apartment. I dressed hurriedly for the ceremony,

and put on my surplice, but neither the Count nor his betrothed appeared. The Count had gone to fetch her from
Dowghielly. They should have come back a long time before
this; but a bride's *toilette* is no little matter, and the doctor
warned the guests that as the breakfast would not be held
until after the religious ceremony, those guests with im-
patient appetites would do well to fortify themselves at a
buffet which was laid with cakes and all sorts of drinks. I
remarked on this occasion how much malice is aroused by
delay; two mothers of pretty girls invited to the wedding
made endless witticisms at the bride's expense.

It was past noon when a salvo of cannon and muskets
heralded her arrival, and soon afterwards a state carriage
entered the avenue, drawn by four magnificent horses. It
was easy to see from the foam which covered their breasts
that the delay had not been on their part. There was no one
in the carriage apart from the bride, Madame Dowghiello,
and the Count. He got out and gave his hand to Madame
Dowghiello. Mademoiselle Iwinska, with a gracefully
coquettish gesture, pretended to hide under her shawl to
avoid the curious looks which surrounded her on all sides.
But she stood up in the carriage, and was just about to take
the Count's hand when the wheelers, terrified perhaps by the
showers of flowers which the peasants were throwing at the
bride, and perhaps also seized with that strange terror which
animals seemed to experience at the sight of Count Szemioth,
reared up and snorted; a wheel struck the corner-post at the
foot of the flight of steps, and for a moment it seemed as if
an accident was about to occur. Mademoiselle Iwinska
uttered a little cry . . . but we were soon reassured, for the
Count snatched her up in his arms and carried her to the top
of the steps as easily as if she had been a dove. We all
applauded his dexterity and his chivalry. The peasants
cheered loudly, and the blushing bride laughed and trembled
at the same time. The Count, who was in no hurry to rid
himself of his charming burden, looked triumphant as he
showed her to the surrounding crowd. . . .

Suddenly, a tall, pale, thin woman, with disordered clothes and dishevelled hair, and every feature on her face drawn with terror, appeared at the top of the flight of stairs without anyone knowing where she had come from.

'A bear!' she shrieked in a piercing voice, 'a bear! . . . Get your guns! . . . He is carrying off a woman! Kill him! Fire! Fire!'

It was the Countess. The bride's arrival had attracted everybody to the entrance and to the courtyard, or to the windows of the castle. Even the women who kept guard over the poor madwoman had forgotten their duties; she had escaped and, without being observed by anyone, had arrived in our midst. It was a most painful scene. She had to be removed, in spite of her cries and resistance. Many of the guests knew nothing about the nature of her illness and it had to be explained to them. People whispered together for a long time after. Every face looked shocked. 'It is an ill omen', said the superstitious, and they are legion in Lithuania.

Meanwhile Mademoiselle Iwinska asked for five minutes to complete her *toilette* and put on her bridal veil, an operation which lasted a full hour. That was more than was required for the people who did not know of the Countess's illness to discover its cause and details.

At last the bride reappeared, magnificently attired and covered with diamonds. Her aunt introduced her to all the guests, and, when the time came to go into the chapel, Madame Dowghiello, to my great astonishment, slapped her niece on the cheek in the presence of the whole company, hard enough to make anyone whose attention was otherwise engaged turn round. This slap was received with perfect equanimity, and no one seemed surprised; but a man in black wrote something on a paper which he had brought with him, and several of the people present signed their names to it with the most nonchalant air. Not until after the ceremony did I discover the answer to the riddle. If I had guessed it, I should have not failed to oppose this odious practice with the whole weight of my sacred office as a minister of religion. It was intended to establish a case for divorce, by pretending that the marriage took place only as the result of physical force exercised against one of the contracting parties.

After the religious service I felt it my duty to address a few words to the young couple, confining myself to putting before them the solemn and sacred nature of the bond by which they had just been united; and, as I still had Mademoiselle Iwinska's frivolous postscript on my mind, I reminded her that she was now entering a new life, no longer accompanied by childish pleasures and amusements but full of serious duties and grave trials. It seemed to me that this part of my sermon produced a considerable effect on the bride, as well as on everyone else who understood German.

Volleys of firing and shouts of joy greeted the procession as it came out of the chapel on its way to the dining-hall. The meal was splendid and appetites very keen; at first no other sound was audible but the clatter of knives and forks. Soon, however, warmed by the champagne and Hungarian wines, the guests began to talk and laugh, and even to shout. The health of the bride was drunk enthusiastically. We had scarcely resumed our seats when an old *pane* with a white moustache stood up and said in a loud voice:

'I am grieved to see that our ancient customs are disappearing. Our forefathers would never have drunk this toast from glasses of crystal. We drank out of the bride's slipper, and even out of her boot; for in my time ladies wore red morocco boots. Let us show, friends, that we are still true Lithuanians. And you, Madame, condescend to give me your slipper.'

'Come and take it, Monsieur', replied the bride, blushing and giving a little laugh; '. . . but I cannot satisfy you with a boot.'

The *pane* did not wait to be asked twice; he went down chivalrously on his knees, took off a little white satin slipper with a red heel, filled it with champagne, and drank so quickly and so adroitly that not more than half was spilt on his clothes. The slipper passed from hand to hand, and all the men drank out of it, but not without difficulty. The old gentleman claimed the slipper as a precious relic, and Madame Dowghiello sent for a maid to bring another pair of shoes for her niece.

This toast was followed by many others, and soon the guests became so noisy that it struck me as improper to remain with them any longer. I escaped from the table without being noticed and went to get some fresh air outside the castle; but there, too, I found a far from edifying spectacle. The servants and the peasants, who had as much beer and spirits as they wished, were for the most part already drunk. There had been quarrelling and some heads broken. Here and there drunken men were lying senseless on the grass, the fête looked rather like a battlefield. I should have been interested to watch the popular dances from close quarters, but most of them were being led by shameless gipsies, and I did not think it becoming to venture into such a crowd. I went back, therefore, to my room and read for some time; then I undressed, and soon fell asleep.

When I awoke the castle clock was striking three o'clock. It was a fine night, although the moon was slightly veiled by a light mist. I tried to go to sleep again, but I could not manage to do so. According to my usual habit when I could not sleep I decided to take a book and read, but I could not find any matches within reach. I got up and was groping my way about the room when a dark body of considerable bulk passed my window and fell with a dull thud into the garden. My first impression was that it was a man, and I thought that one of the drunkards had fallen out of a window. I opened mine and looked out, but I could not see anything. I lit a candle at last, and got back into bed, where I had just finished going through my glossary again when the servant brought me a cup of tea.

Towards eleven o'clock I went to the drawing-room, where I found a good many tired eyes and drawn faces. I learned, in short, that the company had not left the table until a very late hour. Neither the Count nor the young Countess had yet appeared. At half past eleven, after a good many coarse jokes, people began to grumble—at first under their breath, but soon aloud. Dr. Froeber took it upon himself to send the Count's valet to knock at his master's door. In a quarter of an hour the man came back looking anxious, and reported to Dr. Froeber that he had knocked more than a dozen times without obtaining any answer. Madame Dowghiello, the doctor, and I consulted together. The valet's uneasiness had communicated itself to me. We all three went upstairs with him and found the young Countess's maid outside the door. She was very frightened, and declared that something dreadful must have happened, for Madame's window was wide open. I remember with horror that heavy body falling past my window. We knocked loudly; there was no answer. At last the valet brought an iron bar, and we forced the door. . . . No! Courage fails me to describe the scene which presented itself to our eyes. The young Countess was stretched out dead on her bed, her face horribly lacerated, her throat torn open and covered with blood. The Count had disappeared, and no one has heard anything of him since.

The doctor examined the young woman's ghastly wound.

'It was not a steel blade', he exclaimed, 'that made this wound. . . . It was a bite. . . .'

*   *   *

The doctor closed his book, and looked thoughtfully into the fire.

'And is that the end of the story?' asked Adélaïde.

'It is', replied the Professor in a melancholy voice.

'But', she continued, 'why have you called it *Lokis*? No a single person in it bears that name.'

'It is not the name of a man', said the Professor. 'Come Théodore, don't you understand what *Lokis* means?'

'I have no idea.'

'If you were thoroughly acquainted with the law of transformation from Sanskrit into Lithuanian, you would have recognized in *lokis* the Sanskrit *arkcha*, or *rikscha*. *Lokis* is the Lithuanian word for the animal which the Greeks called ἄρκτος, the Latins *ursus*, and the Germans *bär*.

'Now you will understand my epigraph:

> Miszka su Lokiu
> Abu du tokiu.

'You remember that in the *Roman de Renart* the bear is called *Damp Brun*. The Slavs call him Michael, which is Miszka in Lithuanian, and this nickname nearly always replaces the generic name *lokis*. In the same way the French have forgotten their neo-Latin word *goupil*, or *gorpil*, and have substituted *renard*. I could quote you countless other instances. . . .'

But Adélaïde observed that it was late, and we went to bed.

The Abbé Aubain

There is no point in saying how the following letters came into our possession. They strike us as curious, moral, and instructive. We publish them without any change other than the suppression of certain proper names, and of a few passages which have no connexion with the Abbé Aubain's story.

LETTER I

From Madame de P—— to Madame de G——

Noirmoutiers, November 1844

I promised to write to you, my dear Sophie, and I am keeping my word; besides, I have nothing better to do these long evenings.

My last letter informed you how I had made the simultaneous discovery that I was thirty and ruined. For the first of these misfortunes, alas, there is no remedy; as for the second, we have resigned ourselves to it badly enough, but, after all, we are resigned. To repair our fortunes we must pass at least two years in the gloomy manor-house from which I am writing to you. I have been simply heroic. As soon as I learned of the state of our finances, I suggested to Henri that we should go and economize in the country, and a week later we were at Noirmoutiers.

I will not tell you anything of the journey. It was a good many days since I had found myself alone with my husband for such a length of time. Of course, we were both in a bad temper; but, as I was thoroughly determined to put a good face on things, everything went off well. You are familiar with my great resolutions, and you know that I keep them. So now we are settled in. By the way, Noirmoutiers, from a picturesque point of view, leaves nothing to be desired.

There are woods, cliffs, and the sea within a quarter of a league. We have four massive towers, the walls of which are fifteen feet thick. I have fitted out a study in a window-recess. My drawing-room, which is sixty feet long, is decorated with figured tapestry; it is truly magnificent when lighted up by eight candles: that is our Sunday illumination. I die of fright every time I go through it after sunset. It is all very badly furnished, as you may well believe. The doors do not fit properly, the wainscoting creaks, the wind whistles, and the sea roars in the most lugubrious fashion imaginable. Nevertheless, I am beginning to grow accustomed to it.

I tidy up and mend and plant; before the hard frosts set in I shall have made a tolerable billet for myself. You may be certain that your tower will be ready by the spring. If I could only have you in it now! The advantage of Noirmoutiers is that we have no neighbours: we are completely isolated. I am thankful to say I have no other callers but my parish priest, the Abbé Aubain. He is a gentle young man, although he has arched and bushy eyebrows and great dark eyes like those of a stage villain. Last Sunday he gave us quite a fair sermon for the country. It seemed very appropriate. 'Misfortune was a gift from Providence to purify our souls.' So be it. At that rate we ought to give thanks to that honest broker who has tried to purify our souls by taking away all our money.

Good-bye, my dear. My piano has just come, and a great many packing-cases. I must go and unpack them all.

P.S. I reopen this letter to thank you for your present. It is most beautiful, far too beautiful for Noirmoutiers. The grey hood is charming. I recognize your taste there. I shall put it on for Mass on Sunday; perhaps some commercial traveller will be there to admire it. But for whom do you take me, with your novels? I wish to be, I am, a serious-minded person. Have I not good enough reasons? I am going to educate myself. On my return to Paris, three years from now (good gracious, I shall be thirty-three), I mean to be a Philaminte. But really, I do not know what books to ask you to send me. What do you advise me to learn? German or Latin? It would be very pleasant to read *Wilhelm Meister* in the original, or the tales of Hoffmann. Noirmoutiers is the right place for fantastic stories. But how am I to learn German at Noirmoutiers? I should quite like to learn Latin, for I consider it unfair that men should keep it all to themselves. I feel like asking my parish priest to give me lessons. . . .

LETTER II

The same to the same

Noirmoutiers, December 1844

However surprising you may find it, time passes faster than you think, faster than I should have believed myself. What supports my courage most of all is the weakness of my lord and master. Really, men are very inferior to us. He is incredibly depressed and dejected. He gets up as late as he can, rides his horse or goes hunting, or else pays calls on the dullest people imaginable—lawyers and magistrates who live in town, that is to say, six leagues from here. You ought to see him when it is wet! He began reading *Mauprat* a week ago, and he is still on the first volume. 'It is better to praise oneself than to slander others.' That is one of your proverbs. So I will leave him in order to talk of myself.

The country air is doing me incalculable good. I am wonderfully well, and when I look at myself in the glass, (such a glass!) I would not put myself at thirty; but then, I go walking a good deal. Yesterday I managed to get Henri to come with me to the seashore. While he was shooting gulls I read the pirate's song in *The Giaour*. On the beach, facing a rough sea, those fine verses seem finer than ever. Our sea cannot rival that of Greece, but it has its own poetry, like every sea. Do you know what strikes me in Lord Byron? It is his knowledge and understanding of Nature.

He does not talk of the sea merely from having eaten turbot and oysters. He has sailed on it; he has seen storms. All his descriptions are from life. Our poets put rhyme first, then common sense—if there is room for it in the line. While I was walking up and down, reading, looking, and admiring, the Abbé Aubain—I do not know whether I have mentioned my Abbé to you; he is the parish priest of my village—came up and joined me. He is a young priest whom I rather like. He is well-educated and knows 'how to talk with well-bred people'. Besides, from his large dark eyes and pale, melancholy look, I can see that he has an interesting story to tell, and I mean to get him to tell it to me. We talked of the sea, of poetry; and, what will surprise you in a priest of Noirmoutiers, he talks well on those subjects. Then he took me to the ruins of an old abbey on a cliff and pointed out to me a great gateway carved with adorable monsters. Oh, if only I had the money to restore it all! After this, in spite of Henri's remonstrances, for he wanted his dinner, I insisted on going to the presbytery to see a curious reliquary, which the priest had found in a peasant's house. It was indeed very beautiful: a small box in Limoges enamel which would make a lovely jewel-case. But, good gracious, what a house! And we think of ourselves as poor! Imagine a tiny room on the ground floor, badly paved, whitewashed, furnished with a table and four chairs, together with a straw-bottomed armchair, with a little flat cake of a cushion on it, stuffed, I should think, with peach-stones, and covered with red and white check cotton.

On the table there were three or four large Greek or Latin folio volumes. These were the Fathers of the Church, and below, as if hidden away, I found *Jocelyn*. He blushed. He was very attentive, however, in doing the honours of his wretched hovel, without any pride or false modesty. I suspected he had had a romantic adventure: now I had proof of it. In the Byzantine casket which he showed us there was a faded bouquet, five or six years old at least.

'Is that a relic?' I asked him.

'No', he replied, with some agitation. 'I don't know how it came to be there.'

Then he took the bouquet and locked it away carefully in his table drawer. Isn't that clear enough? I went back to the château saddened and encouraged: saddened to have seen such poverty, but encouraged to bear my own, which, beside his, seemed of oriental opulence. You should have seen his surprise when Henri gave him twenty francs for a woman whom he had recommended to us! I really must give him a present. That straw-bottomed arm-chair in which I sat is far too hard. I mean to give him one of those folding iron chairs like that which I took to Italy. You must choose me one, and send it to me as soon as possible. . . .

LETTER III

The same to the same

Noirmoutiers, February 1845

I certainly am not bored at Noirmoutiers. Besides, I have found an interesting occupation, and I have my Abbé to thank for that. He really knows everything, and botany as well. It reminds me of Rousseau's *Letters* to hear the Latin name for a nasty onion, which I had put on the chimney-piece for want of a better place.

'So you know about botany?'

'Not much', he replied; 'just enough to teach the country folk about the herbs which can be useful to them; above all, enough, I must admit, to give a little interest to my solitary walks.'

I thought at once that it would be amusing to pick some pretty flowers on my walks, to dry them, and to arrange them neatly in my old Plutarch.

'Do teach me botany', I said to him.

He wanted to wait until the spring, for there are no flowers at this horrible time of the year.

'But you have some dried flowers', I said; 'I saw them at your house.'

I think I have told you about an old bouquet which he guards jealously. If you could have seen his face! . . . Poor man! I quickly repented of my indiscreet allusion.

To make him forget it I hurriedly told him that he was bound to have a collection of dried plants. This is called a *herbarium*. He agreed at once, and the very next day he brought me in a grey paper parcel, a great many pretty plants, each with its own label. The botany lessons began, and I made astonishing progress from the very start. But I had no idea that botany was so immoral, or that the first explanations would be so difficult especially for a priest.

You see, my dear, plants marry just as we do, but most of them have a great many husbands. Some of them are called *phanerogamous*, if I have remembered that barbarous name properly. It is Greek, and means married publicly at the town hall. Then there are the *cryptogamous*—those who marry secretly. The mushrooms that you eat marry in secret.

All this is very shocking, but he did not come out of it so badly—better than I did, for I was silly enough to burst out laughing once or twice at the most delicate passages. But I have become cautious now, and I do not ask any more questions.

LETTER IV

The same to the same

Noirmoutiers, February 1845

You must insist on having the story of that carefully preserved bouquet; but, the fact is, I dare not ask him for it. In the first place, it is more than probable that there is no story behind it; then, if there is one, perhaps it is a story which he would not like to talk about. For my part, I am quite convinced that . . .

But come, don't let us have any fibbing! You know that I cannot keep any secrets from you. I know this story, and I will tell it to you in a few words; nothing could be easier.

'How is it, Monsieur l'Abbé,' I said to him one day, 'that with your brains and education you came to resign yourself to the care of a little village?'

He replied, with a sad smile:

'It is easier to be the pastor of poor peasants than of townspeople. Everyone must cut his coat according to his cloth.'

'That is why', I said, 'you ought to be in a better position.'

'I was once told', he went on, 'that your uncle, the Bishop of N——, had deigned to think of offering me the living of Sainte-Marie; it is the best in the diocese. Since my old aunt, who is my only surviving relative, lives at N——, people said that it was a very desirable position for me. But I am all right here, and I learnt with pleasure that the bishop had made another choice. What does it matter to me? Am I not happy at Noirmoutiers? If I can do a little good here, it is my place; I ought not to leave it. Besides, town life reminds me of . . .'

He stopped, his eyes turning sad and dreamy, then, recovering himself suddenly, he said:

'We are not working at our botany. . . .'

I was not thinking of the old hay on the table, and I continued my questions.

'When did you take orders?'

'Nine years ago.'

'Nine years ago. . . . But surely you were old enough then to be established in a profession? I do not know why, but I have always imagined that it was not a youthful vocation which led you to become a priest.'

'Alas, no', he said, in an ashamed manner; 'but if my vocation came late, it was determined by causes . . . by a cause . . .'

He became embarrassed and could not finish. As for me, I plucked up my courage.

'I will wager', I said, 'that a certain bouquet, which I have seen, had some part in that determination.'

Hardly had the impertinent question escaped my lips than I could have bitten my tongue off rather than have asked it, but it was too late.

'Why, yes, Madame, that is true; I will tell you all about it, but not today . . . another time. The Angelus is about to ring.'

And he had left before the first stroke of the bell.

I expected some terrible story. He came again the next day, and it was he who took up the conversation of the previous day. He confessed to me that he had loved a young person of N——, but she had a small fortune, and he, a student, had no other resources than his wits. He said to her:

'I am going to Paris, where I hope to obtain a post; you will not forget me, will you, while I am working day and night to make myself worthy of you?'

The young lady was sixteen or seventeen years old, and was very sentimental. She gave him her bouquet as a token of faith. A year later, he heard of her marriage to the solicitor of N—— just as he was about to obtain a chair in a college. He was overwhelmed by the blow, and renounced the post. He told me that for years he could not think of anything else, and he seemed as much moved while telling the story of this very ordinary adventure as if it had only just happened to him. Then he took the bouquet out of his pocket.

'It was childish of me to keep it,' he said, 'perhaps, it was even wrong.'

And he threw it on the fire. When the poor flowers had finished crackling and blazing, he went on in a calmer voice:

'I am grateful to you for having asked me to tell this story. I have you to thank for making me part with a souvenir which it was scarcely seemly for me to keep.'

But his heart was heavy, and it was easy to see how much the sacrifice had cost him. Poor priests! What a life they have! They must forbid themselves the most innocent thoughts, and they are obliged to banish from their hearts all those feelings which make the happiness of other men ... even those memories which are a part of life itself. Priests resemble us unfortunate women, to whom every strong feeling is forbidden as criminal. We are only allowed to suffer, but even then we must hide our pain. Good-bye, I reproach myself for my curiosity, but you were the cause of it.

(*We omit here several letters which do not contain any reference to the Abbé Aubain.*)

LETTER V

The same to the same

Noirmoutiers, May 1845

I have been meaning to write to you for a long time, my dear Sophie, but have always been kept back by a feeling of shame. What I want to tell you is so strange, so ridiculous, and yet so sad, that I scarcely know whether you will be moved to tears or to laughter. I am still at a loss to understand it myself. But I will come to the facts without more ado. I have mentioned the Abbé Aubain to you several times in my previous letters: the parish priest of our village of Noirmoutiers. I also told you the story which led to his entering the priesthood. Living away from everybody, and with my mind full of those melancholy thoughts which you know trouble me, the companionship of an intelligent, cultivated, and agreeable man was extremely congenial to me. Probably I let him see that he interested me, for, after a very short time, he was coming to our house as if he were an old friend. I admit it was quite a novel pleasure for me to talk with a man of superior mind, whose ignorance of the world only enhanced his intellectual distinction. Perhaps, too—for I must tell you everything, and I cannot hide from you any failings of my character—perhaps, too, my coquettish *naïveté* (to use your own expression), for which you have often scolded me, was at work unconsciously. I love to be liked by people I like, and I want to be loved by those I love. . . . I can see you opening your eyes wide at this discourse, and I think I can hear you exclaiming: 'Julie!' Don't worry: I am too old to do anything silly. But to continue. A certain intimacy developed between us without—let me hasten to say—his saying or doing anything inconsistent with his sacred calling. He was very happy in my company. We often talked of his youth, and more than once my evil genius prompted me to bring up the subject of that romantic attachment which brought him a bouquet (now lying in ashes on my hearth) and the melancholy cassock he wears. It was not long before I noticed that he scarcely thought of his faithless mistress any more. One day he had met her in the town, and had even spoken to her. He told me all about it on his return, and added quite calmly that she was happy and had some charming children. He saw, by chance, some of Henri's fits of temper; and the result was some almost unavoidable confidences on my part, and increased sympathy on his. He understood my husband as though he had known him for ten years. Furthermore, his advice was as wise as yours, and more impartial, for you always hold that both sides are in the wrong. He always held that I was in the right, but at the same time recommended prudence and tact. In short, he proved himself a devoted friend. There is something almost feminine about him which captivates me. His character reminds me of yours; it is noble and strong, sensitive and reserved, with an exaggerated sense of duty. . . . I am stringing sentences together in order to delay what I have to tell you. I cannot speak openly; this paper frightens me. If only I had you by the fireside, with a little frame between us, embroidering the same piece of work! But at last, at last, Sophie, I must tell you the real truth. The poor

N

fellow was in love with me. Are you laughing, or are you shocked? I wish I could see you just now. He said nothing to me, of course, but we are scarcely ever mistaken, and those dark eyes of his . . . Just now I believe you are laughing. How many lions of society would like to have those eyes which speak unconsciously! I have seen so many of those gentlemen trying to make theirs expressive and only managing to look idiotic. I must confess that the wicked part of my nature almost rejoiced at first when I recognized the poor fellow's condition. To make a conquest—and a harmless conquest like that—at my age! It is something to be able to excite such a feeling, such an impossible passion! . . . But shame on me! This deplorable feeling soon passed away. I said to myself that I could bring about the ruin of a worthy man by my thoughtless conduct. It was dreadful; I must put a stop to it immediately. I racked my brains to think how I could send him away. One day, we were walking together on the beach at low tide; he did not dare to say a single word to me, and I was equally embarrassed. Five moments of deadly silence followed, during which I picked up shells to cover my confusion. At last I said to him:

'My dear Abbé, you really must be given a better living than this. I shall write to my uncle, the bishop; I will go to see him if necessary.'

'Leave Noirmoutiers!' he exclaimed, clasping his hands together. 'But I am so happy here! What more can I desire, now that you are here? You have quite spoilt me, and my little presbytery has become a palace.'

'No,' I replied, 'my uncle is very old; if I had the misfortune to lose him I should not know whom to address to obtain a suitable post for you.'

'Alas, Madame, I should be very sorry to leave this village! . . . The parish priest of Sainte-Marie has died . . . but I am not worried, because I believe he will be replaced by the Abbé Raton, who is a most excellent priest. I am delighted about this, for if Monseigneur had thought of me . . .'

'The Curé of Sainte-Marie has died!' I exclaimed. 'I shall go to see my uncle at N—— today.'

'Ah, Madame, don't do anything of the sort. The Abbé Raton is much better fitted for the living than I; and, besides, to leave Noirmoutiers . . . !'

'Monsieur l'Abbé,' I said resolutely, *'you must!'*

At these words he bowed his head and did not dare to raise any further objections. I nearly ran back to the château. He followed me a couple of paces behind, poor man, too upset to open his mouth. He was quite crushed. I did not lose a minute. By eight o'clock I was at my uncle's house. I found him greatly prejudiced in favour of his Raton; but he is fond of me, and I know my power. At last, after a long discussion, I got my way. Raton has been put aside, and the Abbé Aubain is Curé of Sainte-Marie. He has been in town for two days. The poor fellow understood my *'You must'*. He thanked me gravely, and spoke of nothing but his gratitude. I am grateful to him for leaving Noirmoutiers so quickly, and for telling me even, that he was in a hurry to go and thank Monseigneur. On leaving, he sent me his pretty Byzantine casket, and asked permission to write to me sometimes. Well, my dear? *Are you satisfied, Coucy?*[1] This is a lesson which I shall not forget when I return to society. But then I shall be thirty-three, and will have little reason to fear being loved . . . and with a love such as his! . . . That would be quite out of the question. Never mind, this folly has left me with a pretty casket and a true friend. When I am forty, and a grandmother, I will plot to obtain the Abbé Aubain a living in Paris. Some day you will see this come to pass, my dear, and he will give your daughter her first communion.

[1] A quotation from Voltaire's *Adélaïde du Guesclin* [Trans.].

LETTER VI

*The Abbé Aubain to the Abbé Bruneau, Professor of Theology at
                          Saint-A——*

N——, *May 1845*

My dear Professor—It is the Curé of Sainte-Marie who is
writing to you, and no longer the humble parish priest of
Noirmoutiers. I have left my marshes, and now I am a towns-
man, installed in a fine living, in the main street of N——;
in charge of a large, well-built, well-maintained church, of
splendid architecture, depicted in every album in France.
The first time that I said Mass here, before a marble altar,
which glittered with gilding, I had to ask myself if it really
was myself. But it is true enough, and one of my joys is the
hope that during your holidays you will come and pay me a
visit. I shall have a comfortable room to offer you, and a
good bed, not to mention a certain claret which I call my
Noirmoutiers claret, and which I venture to say is worthy
of you. But, you will ask me, how did I get from Noirmoutiers to Sainte-Marie? You left me at the entrance to
the nave, you find me now at the steeple.

O Meliboe, deus nobis haec otia fecit.

Providence, my dear Professor, sent a grand lady from
Paris to Noirmoutiers. Misfortunes of a kind we shall never
know had temporarily reduced her to an income of 10,000
crowns per annum. She is an agreeable and good woman,
unfortunately a little spoilt by frivolous reading, and by
association with the dandies of the capital. Bored to death
by a husband for whom there is little to be said, she did me
the honour of taking an interest in me. There were endless
presents and continual invitations, then every day some
fresh scheme in which I was wanted. 'Monsieur l'Abbé, I
want to learn Latin. . . . Monsieur l'Abbé, I want to be
taught botany.' *Horresco referens*, did she not also want me to
expound theology to her? If only you had been there, my
dear Professor! In short, to quench such a thirst for know-

ledge we would have required all the professors of Saint-
A——. Fortunately, her whims never lasted for long: the
course of studies rarely went as far as the third lesson. When
I told her that the Latin for rose was *rosa*, she exclaimed:
'What a well of learning you are, Monsieur l'Abbé! How
could you have allowed yourself to be buried at Noirmoutiers?' To tell you the truth, my dear Professor, the
good lady, through reading the wicked books that are produced nowadays, got all sorts of queer ideas into her head.
One day she lent me a book which she had just received
from Paris, and which had enraptured her: *Abélard*, by
Monsieur de Rémusat. No doubt you have read it, and
admired the author's learned research, unfortunately carried
out in so wrong a spirit. At first I turned to the second
volume, containing the 'Philosophy of Abélard', and, after
reading that with the greatest interest, I went back to the
first, to the life of the great heresiarch. This, of course, was
all that Madame had deigned to read. That, my dear Professor, opened my eyes. I realized that there was danger in
the company of fine ladies so greatly enamoured of learning.
This one could give points to Héloïse in the matter of
infatuation. This situation, so new to me, was troubling me
greatly when, suddenly, she said to me: 'Monsieur l'Abbé,
the incumbent of Sainte-Marie is dead, and you must have
the living. *You Must*.' Immediately she drove off in her
carriage to see Monseigneur; and, a few days later, I was
Curé of Sainte-Marie, somewhat ashamed of having obtained the living by favour, but otherwise delighted to be
out of reach of the clutches of a lioness from the capital. A
lioness, my dear Professor, is the Parisian expression for a
woman of fashion.

ʼΩ Ζεῦ, γυναικῶν οἷον ὤπάσὰς γένος.[2]

Ought I to have rejected this good fortune in order to

[2] A line taken, I believe, from the *Seven Against Thebes* of Aeschylus; 'O
Jupiter! Women! . . . What a race you have given us!' The Abbé Aubain
and his Professor, the Abbé Bruneau, are good classical scholars.

defy temptation? What a fool I should have been! Did not St. Thomas of Canterbury accept castles from Henry II? Good-bye, my dear Professor. I look forward to discussing philosophy with you in a few months' time, each of us in a comfortable arm-chair, before a plump chicken and a bottle of claret, *more philosophorum. Vale et me ama.*

Il Viccolo[1] di Madama Lucrezia

I WAS twenty-three years old when I set out for Rome. My father gave me a dozen letters of introduction, only one of which, a missive no less than four pages long, was sealed. It was addressed: 'To the Marchesa Aldobrandi'.

'You must write and tell me if the Marchesa is still beautiful', said my father.

Now, from my earliest childhood, I had seen over the mantelpiece in his study a miniature of a very lovely woman, with powdered hair crowned with ivy, and a tiger skin over her shoulder. Underneath was the inscription, 'Roma, 18—'. The dress struck me as so strange that I had often asked who the lady was.

'She is a Bacchante', was the only answer given me.

But this reply scarcely satisfied me. I even suspected a secret behind it; for at this simple question my mother would purse her lips, and my father would assume a serious expression.

This time, when giving me the sealed letter, he glanced furtively at the portrait; involuntarily I did the same, and the idea occurred to me that the powdered Bacchante might perhaps be the Marchesa Aldobrandi. As I was beginning to understand the ways of this world I drew all kinds of conclusions from my mother's expression and my father's glance.

When I reached Rome, the first letter I delivered was the one to the Marchesa. She lived in a beautiful palace close to St. Mark's Square.

I gave my letter and my card to a servant in yellow livery,

[1] In Italian the word *vicolo* [little street] has only one 'c'. I have retained Mérimée's eccentric spelling of the word in this story. (Translator's note.)

who showed me into a vast drawing-room, which was dark and gloomy and poorly furnished. But in all Roman palaces there are pictures by old masters; this room contained a great number of them, several of which were very remarkable.

The first one I noticed was a portrait of a woman which I thought was a Leonardo da Vinci. From the magnificence of the frame, and the rosewood easel on which it rested, there could be no doubt that it was the chief treasure of the collection. As the Marchesa was a long time coming, I was able to examine it at leisure. I even carried it to a window to see it in a better light. It was obviously a portrait and not an imaginary study, for faces like that cannot be invented: she was a beautiful woman, with rather thick lips, eyebrows nearly joined together, and an expression which was both haughty and affectionate. In the background was her coat of arms, surmounted by a ducal coronet. But what struck me most was that her dress, down to the powder on her hair, was the same as that of my father's Bacchante.

I was holding the portrait in my hand when the Marchesa entered.

'Just like his father!' she cried, coming towards me. 'Ah, you French! You French! He has hardly arrived before he seizes upon *Madama Lucrezia*.'

I hastened to apologize for my impertinence, and launched into endless praises of the masterpiece by Leonardo which I had been so bold as to remove from its place.

'It is indeed a Leonardo', said the Marchesa, 'and it is the portrait of the infamous Lucrezia Borgia. Of all my pictures it is the one your father admired most. . . . But, heavens, what a resemblance! It is as if I were looking at your father as he was twenty-five years ago. How is he? What is he doing? And will he not come to see us in Rome some time?'

Although the Marchesa was wearing neither tiger skin nor powder on her hair, at the first glance, with my quick perception, I recognized in her my father's Bacchante. Some twenty-five years had not been able entirely to deface the traces of great beauty. Only her expression had changed, like her dress. She was clothed completely in black, and her treble chin, her grave smile, and her serious yet radiant manner, told me that she had turned pious.

No one could have given me a warmer welcome; in a few words she offered me her home, her purse, and her friends, among whom she mentioned several cardinals.

'Look upon me', she said, 'as your mother...' She lowered her eyes modestly. 'Your father has asked me to look after you and to advise you.'

And to show me that she did not intend her office to be a sinecure she began at once by putting me on my guard against the dangers Rome had for young men of my age, and earnestly exhorted me to avoid them. I must shun bad company, artists especially, and only associate with the people she would recommend to me. In short, I was treated to a regular sermon. I replied respectfully, and with fitting hypocrisy.

'I am afraid that my son the Marchese is away on our estate in Romagna', she said, as I rose to go, 'but I will introduce you to my second son, Don Ottavio, who will soon become a Monsignor. I hope you will like him, and that you will become friends as you ought to....'

She added hurriedly: 'For you are about the same age, and he is a quiet, steady boy like yourself.'

She sent immediately for Don Ottavio, and I was presented to a tall, pale young man, with downcast melancholy eyes, who already had a sanctimonious air.

Without giving him time to speak, the Marchesa made me the readiest offers of service in his name. He assented by making a deep bow at each of his mother's suggestions, and it was arranged that the very next day he should show me round the town and bring me back to dinner *en famille* at the Aldobrandi palace.

I had hardly gone twenty steps down the street when an imperious voice called out behind me:

'Where are you going alone at this hour, Don Ottavio?'

I turned round and saw a fat priest, who looked me up and down from head to foot with his eyes wide open.

'I am not Don Ottavio', I said.

The priest bowed down to the ground, offering profuse apologies, and a moment later I saw him go into the Aldobrandi palace. I continued on my way, not particularly flattered at being taken for a budding Monsignor.

In spite of the Marchesa's warnings, indeed perhaps because of them, my next step was to look for the lodging of a painter I knew, and I spent an hour with him in his studio talking over the legitimate or dubious ways of enjoying oneself that Rome could offer me. I led him on to the subject of the Aldobrandi family.

The Marchesa, he told me, after being excessively frivolous, became extremely devout when she had recognized that she was too old for further conquests. Her elder son was a fool, who spent his time hunting and collecting the rents of the farms on his vast estates. They were in the process of making an idiot of the second son, Don Ottavio, whom they intended to be a cardinal some day. Meanwhile he was in the clutches of the Jesuits. He never went out alone; he was forbidden to look at a woman, or to take a single step without having at his heels the priest who had brought him up for God's service, and who, after having been the Marchesa's last *amico*, now ruled her house with an almost despotic authority.

The next day Don Ottavio, accompanied by the Abbé Negroni, the priest who had taken me for his pupil the previous day, came for me in a carriage and offered his services as a guide.

The first monument we stopped at was a church. Following his priest's example, Don Ottavio knelt down, beat his breast, and made countless signs of the cross. After he had got up he showed me the frescoes and statues, and talked to me about them like a man of sense and taste. This was an agreeable surprise to me; we began to talk, and his conversation pleased me. For some time we conversed in Italian, but suddenly he said to me in French:

'My director does not understand a word of your language; let us talk French, and we shall feel freer.'

It was as if the change of language had transformed the young man. There was nothing that smacked of the priest in his talk. I could have imagined him to be one of our liberals from the provinces. I noticed that he said everything in an even, monotonous tone of voice, which often contrasted strangely with the vivacity of his expressions. It was, apparently, a ruse to deceive Negroni, who from time to time asked us to explain what we were talking about. I need hardly say that our translation was extremely free.

A young man in violet stockings passed us.

'That is one of our modern patricians', said Don Ottavio. 'What an infamous livery! And it will be mine in a few months! What happiness,' he added after a moment's silence, 'what happiness to live in a country like yours! If I were a Frenchman I might perhaps become a deputy one day.'

This lofty ambition made me want to laugh, and as the Abbé noticed this, I had to explain that we were talking of the error of an archaeologist who mistook a statue by Bernini for an ancient work.

We dined at the Aldobrandi palace. Immediately after coffee the Marchesa asked me to excuse her son, who was obliged to retire to his room to carry out certain pious duties. I remained alone with her and the Abbé Negroni, who, lying back in a big arm-chair slept the sleep of the just.

In the meantime the Marchesa questioned me closely about my father, about Paris, about my past life, and about my future plans. She seemed to me a kind and amiable woman, but rather too inquisitive and above all too concerned about my salvation. But she spoke Italian admirably, and I took a lesson in pronunciation from her which I promised myself I would repeat.

I often came back to see her. Nearly every morning I visited ancient monuments with her son and the ever-

present Negroni, and in the evenings I dined with them at
the Aldobrandi palace. The Marchesa entertained very
rarely, and then nearly always ecclesiastics.

Once, however, she introduced me to a German lady, who
was a recent convert and a close friend of hers. She was a
certain Frau von Strahlenheim, a very handsome woman
who had been living in Rome for a long time. While the
ladies were talking together about a celebrated preacher, I
studied by the light of the lamp the portrait of Lucrezia,
until I felt it incumbent upon me to put in a word.

'What eyes!' I exclaimed. 'Anyone would swear that these
eyelids were about to move!'

At this somewhat pretentious comment, which I had made
to convince Frau von Strahlenheim that I was a connoisseur,
she trembled with fear and hid her face in her handkerchief.

'What is the matter, my dear?' said the Marchesa.

'Oh, nothing. Only what this gentleman said just now!...'

We pressed her with questions, and when she said that
my words had reminded her of a horrible story, we compelled
her to recount it.

Here it is in a few words:

Frau von Strahlenheim had a sister-in-law called Wilhelmina, who was engaged to a young man from West-
phalia, Julius von Katzenellenbogen, a volunteer in General
Kleist's division. I am sorry to have to repeat so many
barbarous names, but extraordinary adventures never
happen except to people with names which are difficult to
pronounce.

Julius was a charming fellow, full of patriotism and metaphysics. He had given his portrait to Wilhelmina when he
had joined the army and she had given him hers, which he
always wore next to his heart. They do this sort of thing in
Germany.

On 13 September 1813 Wilhelmina was at Kassel. She was
sitting in a drawing-room, about five o'clock in the afternoon, busy knitting with her mother and her sister-in-law.
While she was working she looked at her fiancé's portrait,

which was standing on a little work-table in front of her. Suddenly she gave a terrible cry, put her hand on her heart, and fainted. They had the greatest difficulty in the world in bringing her back to consciousness, and, as soon as she could speak, she said:

'Julius is dead! He has been killed!'

She insisted that she had seen the portrait shut its eyes, and that at the same moment she had felt a terrible pain, as though a red-hot iron had pierced her heart: her horror-struck features were proof of her sincerity.

Everybody tried in vain to convince her that her vision was unreal and that she ought to pay no attention to it. The poor child was inconsolable; she spent the night in tears and wanted to go into mourning the next day, as if she were already convinced of the affliction which had been revealed to her.

Two days later, news came of the bloody battle of Leipzig. Julius had written his fiancée a letter dated three o'clock in the afternoon of the 13th. He had not been wounded, but had distinguished himself, and had just entered Leipzig, where he expected to spend the night at headquarters, which were, of course, out of range of any danger. This reassuring letter did not calm Wilhelmina, who noticed that it had been written at three o'clock, and persisted in believing that her beloved had died at five.

The unfortunate girl was not mistaken. It was soon learnt that Julius had been sent out of Leipzig with a dispatch at half-past four, and that three-quarters of a league from the town, beyond the Elster, a straggler from the enemy army, concealed in a ditch, had fired at him and killed him. The bullet had pierced his heart and broken the portrait of Wilhelmina.

'And what became of the poor girl?' I asked Frau von Strahlenheim.

'Oh! she was very ill. She is married now to a gentleman who is a magistrate in Werner, and, if you went to Dessau, she would show you Julius's portrait.'

'All that was done through the intervention of the devil', the Abbé broke in, for he had only been half asleep during Frau von Strahlenheim's story. 'He who could make the heathen oracles speak could easily make the eyes of a portrait move if he thought fit. Not twenty years ago an Englishman was strangled by a statue at Tivoli.'

'By a statue!' I exclaimed. 'How did that come about?'

'He was a lord who had been carrying out excavations at Tivoli, and had discovered a statue of an Empress, Agrippina, Messalina . . . it matters little which. He had taken it to his house, and by dint of gazing at it and admiring it, he fell madly in love with it. All those Protestants are already more than half mad anyway. He called it his wife, his lady, and kissed it, marble as it was. He said that the statue came to life every evening for his benefit. And this was so true that one morning they found milord stone dead in his bed. Well, would you believe it?—another Englishman came along who was quite ready to buy the statue. Now I would have had it made into lime.'

Once people have started telling stories of the supernatural, there is no stopping them. Everybody has his story to tell, and I myself contributed to this collection of fearful tales; with the result that when we separated we were all rather scared and full of respect for the devil's power.

I walked back to my lodgings, and, to get into the Corso, I took a little winding lane which was unfamiliar to me. It was quite deserted. I could see nothing but long garden walls, or a few mean-looking houses, none of which was lighted up. It had just struck midnight, and the sky was dark and threatening. I was in the middle of the street, walking quite fast, when I heard a slight noise above my head, a hiss, and at the same moment a rose fell at my feet. I raised my eyes and, in spite of the darkness, I saw a woman dressed in white at a window, with one arm stretched out towards me. Now we French are very conceited when we are abroad, for our forefathers, the conquerors of Europe, have nourished us on tradition flattering to our national pride. I believed whole-heartedly in the susceptibility of all German, Spanish, and Italian ladies to the mere sight of a Frenchman. In short, at that time I was still very much of a Frenchman and, besides, did not the rose tell its own tale plainly enough?

'Madame,' I said in a low voice as I picked up the rose, 'you have dropped your posy. . . .'

But the woman had already vanished, and the window had been closed noiselessly. I did what any other man would have done in my position: I looked for the nearest door, which was only two steps from the window; I found it, and I waited to have it opened for me. Five minutes went by in a profound silence; then I coughed, and after that I scratched softly; but the door did not open. I examined it more carefully, hoping to find a key or a latch; to my great surprise I found that it was padlocked.

'So the jealous lover has not come home yet?' I said to myself.

I picked up a small stone and threw it against the window; it hit a wooden shutter and fell at my feet.

'The devil!' I thought; 'Roman ladies must be accustomed to lovers who carry ladders in their pockets; no one had told me of that custom.'

I waited a few more minutes, but just as fruitlessly. Only I thought once or twice that I saw the shutter tremble slightly, as if someone inside were trying to push it aside to look into the street. My patience was exhausted at the end of a quarter of an hour. I lit a cigar and went on my way, but not until I had carefully taken stock of the position of the padlocked house.

The next day, thinking over this adventure, I arrived at the following conclusions: a young Roman lady, probably of great beauty, had noticed me on my expeditions about the town, and had been attracted by my modest charms. If she had declared her passion only by the gift of a mysterious flower, it was because she was restrained by a becoming sense of modesty, or else because she had been disturbed by the presence of some duenna, or perhaps by some cursed guardian like Rosina's Bartolo. I decided to lay siege to the house inhabited by this *Infanta*.

With this admirable intention I left my rooms after giving my hair a determined brushing and putting on my new frock-coat and yellow gloves. In this outfit, with my hat tilted over one ear and the faded rose in my buttonhole, I set off for the street whose name I did not yet know, but which I had no difficulty in discovering. A notice over a Madonna told me that it was called *Il Viccolo di Madama Lucrezia*.

I was struck by this name, which immediately reminded me of Leonardo da Vinci's portrait, together with the stories of presentiments and witchcraft which I had heard the evening before at the Marchesa's. Then I reflected that some matches are made in heaven. Why should not my love be called Lucrezia? Why should she not look like the Lucrezia in the Aldobrandi collection?

It was broad daylight, I was a few steps away from a ravishing young lady, and no sinister thoughts entered into the emotion I felt.

I came to the house. It was No. 13—an unlucky omen. . . ! Alas, it hardly corresponded to the idea I had conceived of it after seeing it by night. It was certainly no palace—far from it. The walls surrounding it were blackened with age and covered with moss, and overhanging them were the branches of some fruit trees which had been carelessly pruned. In one corner of the enclosure was a pavilion two stories high, with two windows looking on to the street; both were closed by old shutters furnished outside with numerous iron bars. The door was a low one, and over it was a faded coat of arms; it was closed, as on the previous night, by a large padlock which was attached to a chain. On this door were chalked the words: *House To Let or For Sale*.

However, I had not made a mistake. On this side of the street the houses were too few for any confusion to be possible. It was indeed my padlock, and furthermore, two rose-petals on the pavement near the door indicated the exact spot where I had received the material declaration of love from my beloved, and also proved that the pavement in front of her house was rarely swept.

I asked a few poor people of the neighbourhood if they could tell me where the caretaker of this mysterious house lived.

'Not here', they replied curtly.

My question seemed to displease those to whom I put it; and this piqued my curiosity still further. Going from door to door, I ended up by entering a kind of dark cellar, where there was an old woman who might have been suspected of witchcraft, for she had a black cat and was cooking some mysterious decoction in a cauldron.

'You want to look over the house of Madama Lucrezia?' she said. 'I have the key.'

'All right. Show me over it.'

'Would you like to rent it?' she asked, smiling with a dubious air.

'Yes, if it suits me.'

'It won't suit you; but look, will you give me a *paul* if I show you over it?'

'Willingly.'

On this assurance she jumped up from her stool, un-hooked a rusty key from the wall, and led me to No. 13.

'Why', I said, 'is this house called Lucrezia's house?'

'Why are you called a foreigner?' retorted the old woman, with a chuckle. 'Isn't it because you *are* a foreigner?'

'All right. But who was this Madama Lucrezia? Was she a Roman lady?'

'What! You come to Rome, and you've never heard of Madama Lucrezia? I'll tell you her story when we're inside. But here's some more devilry! I don't know what's wrong with this key—it won't turn. You try it.'

True enough, the padlock and the key had not seen each other for a long time. However, with the help of three or four oaths and much grinding of my teeth, I succeeded in turning the key in the lock; but I tore my yellow gloves and

o

strained the palm of my hand. We entered a dark passage, which gave access to several low rooms.

The curiously panelled ceilings were covered with cob-webs, under which traces of gilding could just be seen. From the damp smell which came from every room it was obvious that they had not been occupied for a long time. There was not a single piece of furniture in them, only some strips of old leather hanging down the damp walls. From the carving of a few consoles and the shape of the chimney-pieces I concluded that the house dated from the fifteenth century, and probably in the past it had been tastefully decorated. The windows had little panes of glass, most of which were broken and looked out on to the garden, where I noticed a rose tree in flower, a few fruit trees, and a great deal of broccoli.

When I had wandered through all the rooms on the ground floor, I went upstairs to the storey where I had seen my mysterious lady. The old woman tried to keep me back by telling me there was nothing to see and that the staircase was in a very bad state. Seeing that I was determined to go up-stairs, she followed me, but with marked aversion. The rooms on this floor were very much like the others, only they were not so damp, and the floors and windows, too, were in a better state. In the last room that I entered, there was a large black leather arm-chair, which, strangely enough, was not covered with dust. I sat down in it, and finding it comfortable enough for listening to a story, I asked the old woman to tell me the tale of Madama Lucrezia; but first of all, in order to refresh her memory, I gave her a few *pauls*. She cleared her throat, blew her nose, and began as follows:

'In heathen times, when Alexander was Emperor, he had a daughter who was as beautiful as the day. She was called Madama Lucrezia. Look—there she is!'

I turned round quickly. The old woman was pointing to a carved console which supported the chief beam of the room. It was a crude carving of a siren.

'Goodness,' the old woman went on, 'how she loved to enjoy herself! And, as her father might have found fault with her for this, she had this house built.

'Every night she came down from the Quirinal and came here to amuse herself. She used to stand at that window, and when a handsome cavalier like you passed by in the street, she called to him, and I leave you to guess whether he was well-received. But men are talkative, or at least some of them are, and they could have done her harm by their babbling, so she took her precautions. When she had taken leave of her lover, her soldiers were standing on the staircase by which we came up. They dispatched him, and then buried him among the broccoli! Yes, some of their bones have been found in the garden.

'This went on for a long time, but one evening her brother, Sisto Tarquino, passed under her window. She did not recognize him, and she called to him. He came up. In the dark all cats look grey, and he was treated like all the rest. But he had left his handkerchief behind, and his name was on it.

'Despair seized her as soon as she saw what had happened. She undid her garter straight away and hung herself from that beam up there. What an example for young people!'

While the old woman was thus confusing the ages, mixing up the Tarquins with the Borgias, I had my eyes fixed on the floor. I had just noticed some rose-petals which were still fresh, and this gave me furiously to think.

'Who looks after this garden?' I asked the old woman.

'My son, the gardener of Signor Vanozzi, who owns the garden next door. Signor Vanozzi is always away in the Maremma; and he hardly ever comes to Rome. That's why the garden isn't very nicely kept. My son is with him, and I'm afraid they won't be coming back for a long time', she added with a sigh.

'He has plenty to do, then, with Signor Vanozzi?'

'Oh, he's a queer man, who keeps him busy with far too

many things. I'm afraid there's some shady business afoot.
. . . Ah, my poor son!'

She took a step towards the door as if she wanted to break
off the conversation.

'No one lives here, then?' I went on, stopping her.

'Not a soul.'

'And why is that?'

She shrugged her shoulders.

'Listen to me', I said, giving her a piastre.

'Tell me the truth. There's a woman who comes here.'

'A woman? Mercy on us!'

'Yes, I saw her yesterday evening and I spoke to her.'

'Holy Mother!' cried the old woman, rushing towards the
staircase. 'That must have been Madama Lucrezia! Let's go!
Let's go! They did tell me she came back here at night, but I
didn't want to tell you for fear of spoiling the landlord's
chances, because I thought you wanted to rent the place.'

It was out of the question to hold her back. She was in a
hurry to leave the house, anxious, she said, to light a candle
in the nearest church.

I went out too, and let her go, despairing of learning anything more from her.

You will readily guess that I did not tell the story of my
adventures at the Aldobrandi palace; the Marchesa was too
prudish, and Don Ottavio too much taken up with politics
to give any useful advice in a love affair. But I went to see
my artist friend, who knew everything there was to know
about Rome, and asked him what he thought of it.

'I think you have seen the ghost of Lucrezia Borgia', he
said. 'What danger you have been in! She was dangerous
enough when she was alive; imagine what she must be like
now she is dead! It makes me shudder to think of it.'

'Joking apart, what can it have been?'

'So you're an atheist and a philosopher and don't believe
in the most orthodox explanations. Very well, then. What
do you say of this other hypothesis? Suppose the old woman
lets the house to women who are capable of accosting men

who pass by in the street; there are old women sufficiently
depraved to practise that profession.'

'Wonderful', I said. 'Then I must look like a saint, for the
old woman never offered any services of that sort. You insult
me. Besides, old fellow, remember the furnishing of the
house: a man must be possessed by the devil to be satisfied
with it.'

'Then there's no doubt about it: it's a ghost. But wait a
bit, I have another idea. You mistook the house. Yes, now
that I think about it: near a garden, with a little low
door . . . ? Why, that's my dear friend Rosina's! Less than
eighteen months ago she was the ornament of that street.
It's true that she's gone blind in one eye, but that's a trifle.
. . . She still has a very lovely profile.'

None of these explanations satisfied me. When evening
came I walked slowly past Lucrezia's house, but I did not
see anything. I went past it again with no further result.
Three or four evenings in succession, I hung about under
its windows on my way home from the Aldobrandi palace,
still without any success. I had begun to forget the mysterious
occupant of No. 13, when, walking along the street towards
midnight, I distinctly heard a woman's laugh behind the
shutter of the window at which the girl with the rose had
appeared to me. Twice I heard that little laugh, and I could
not help feeling slightly afraid when at the same time I saw
a group of hooded penitents appear at the other end of the
street, with tapers in hand, bearing a corpse to burial. When
they had gone by I took up my stand once more under the
window; but now I heard nothing more. I tried throwing
pebbles, and even called out more or less loudly; but still
no one appeared; and when a heavy shower came on, I was
obliged to beat a retreat.

I am ashamed to say how many times I stopped outside
that accursed house without succeeding in solving the riddle
which tormented me. Only once did I pass along the Viccolo
di Madama Lucrezia with Don Ottavio and his inseparable
Abbé.

'That is Lucrezia's house', I said.

I saw him change colour.

'Yes', he replied; 'a very vague popular tradition asserts that this was Lucrezia Borgia's house of assignation. If those walls could speak, what horrors they could reveal to us! All the same, my friend, when I compare those times with our own I find myself regretting them. Under Alexander VI there were still Romans. Now there are none. Caesar Borgia was a monster; but he was a great man. He tried to turn the barbarians out of Italy; and perhaps, if his father had lived, he might have accomplished that great plan. Oh, if only Heaven would send us a tyrant like Borgia to deliver us from these human despots who are degrading us!'

When Don Ottavio launched out into the realms of politics, it was impossible to stop him. By the time we reached the Piazza del Popolo, his panegyric in favour of enlightened despotism was still not finished, and we were a thousand miles from the subject of my own Lucrezia.

One evening, when I had called to pay my respects to the Marchesa at a very late hour, she told me her son was unwell, and begged me to go up to his room. I found him lying fully dressed on his bed, reading a French newspaper which I had sent him that morning concealed inside a volume of the Fathers of the Church. An edition of the Holy Fathers had for some time served us for those communications which had to be concealed from the Abbé and the Marchesa. On days when the post arrived from France, I received a folio volume. I returned another, into which I slipped a newspaper, lent to me by the Ambassador's secretary. This gave the Marchesa an excellent opinion of my piety; and also impressed her spiritual director, who sometimes tried to get me to discuss theology with him.

When I had talked for some time with Don Ottavio, and had noticed that he seemed so unwell that not even politics could arouse his interest, I recommended him to undress, and I took leave of him. It was a cold night and I had no cloak with me. Don Ottavio urged me to take his; I accepted, and received a lesson in the difficult art of wearing a cloak in the proper Roman fashion.

I left the Aldobrandi palace muffled up to the eyes. I had taken only a few steps along the pavement of St. Mark's Square when a man of the people, whom I had noticed sitting on a bench by the gate of the palace, came up to me and held out a crumpled piece of paper.

'Read that, for the love of God!' he said, and promptly disappeared, running as fast as his legs would carry him.

I took the paper, and looked round for a light by which to read it. By the light of a lamp burning in front of a Madonna, I saw that it was a pencilled note, written apparently in a trembling hand. I had considerable difficulty in making out the following words:

'Do not come tonight, or we are lost! All is known except your name. Nothing can part us. Your LUCREZIA.'

'Lucrezia!' I cried. 'Lucrezia again! What devilish mystification is there behind all this? "Do not come." But, my beauty, which is the road that leads to your house?'

While I was thinking about this note I mechanically set off in the direction of the Viccolo di Madama Lucrezia, and soon found myself in front of No. 13.

The street was as deserted as usual, and only the sound of my footsteps disturbed the profound silence reigning all around. I stopped and looked up at the window I knew so well. This time I was not mistaken: the shutter was opening.

Now the window was wide open.

I thought I saw a human form standing out against the dark background of the room.

'Lucrezia, is that you?' I said in a low voice.

No one answered, but I heard a clicking noise, the cause of which I could not at first understand.

'Lucrezia, is that you?' I repeated rather louder.

At the same moment I received a terrible blow in the chest, there was the sound of a report, and I found myself stretched out on the ground.

'Take that from the Signora Lucrezia!' cried a hoarse voice, and the shutter was silently closed.

I promptly staggered to my feet, and the first thing I did was to feel myself all over, as I expected to find a big hole in my stomach. The cloak and my coat were both pierced, but the impact of the bullet had been deadened by the folds of the cloth, and I had escaped with nothing worse than a bad bruise.

The idea that a second shot might not be long in coming made me drag myself over to that inhospitable house straight away, and I kept close to the walls so that no one could take aim at me.

I was moving away as quickly as I could, still panting for breath, when a man whom I had not noticed behind me took my arm and asked me anxiously if I were hurt.

From his voice I recognized Don Ottavio. It was not the moment to question him, however surprised I was to see him alone and in the street at that time of night. I told him briefly that I had just been fired at from a certain window, but that I had only been bruised.

'It's a mistake!' he cried. 'But I can hear people coming. Can you walk? If we are seen together I should be done for; but I won't abandon you.'

He took my arm and led me along at a rapid pace. We walked, or rather ran, as far as I could go; but I was soon obliged to sit down on a cornerstone to get my breath back.

Fortunately we were by that time not far from a large house where a ball was being held. There were a great many carriages in front of the door, and Don Ottavio went to find one, put me inside, and took me to my hotel. After drinking a large glass of water I felt quite recovered and told him in detail all that had happened to me in front of that fateful house, from the gift of the rose to that of the bullet.

He listened with his head bowed, half hidden in one of his hands. When I showed him the note that I had received, he seized it and read it eagerly.

'It's a mistake, a horrible mistake!' he exclaimed again.

'You will admit, my dear fellow,' I said to him, 'that it's a very unpleasant mistake for both of us. I might have been killed, and there are about a dozen holes in your fine cloak. Heavens, how jealous your fellow-countrymen are!'

Don Ottavio pressed my hands, looking the picture of woe, and read the note again without answering.

'Do try', I said, 'to offer me some explanation of this affair. I'll be damned if I can make anything of it!'

He shrugged his shoulders.

'At least tell me what I ought to do', I said. 'To whom should I complain in your holy city, in order to see justice done to this gentleman who peppers passers-by without even asking them their names? I confess I should be delighted to see him hanged.'

'Don't do anything of the sort', he cried. 'You don't know this country. Don't say a word to anyone of what has happened to you. You would be running too great a risk.'

'What should I be risking? Dammit all, I mean to have my revenge. If I had offended the scoundrel there might be some excuse; but just because I picked up a rose . . . in all conscience, I surely don't deserve a bullet.'

'Leave it to me', said Don Ottavio; 'perhaps I shall succeed in clearing up the mystery. But I ask you as a special favour, as a signal proof of your friendship for me, not to mention this to a single soul. Will you promise me that?'

He looked so sad as he said this that I had not the heart to resist him, and I promised him all he asked. He thanked me effusively, and, after he had himself applied a compress of eau-de-Cologne to my chest, he shook hands with me and bade me farewell.

'By the way,' I asked him, as he was opening the door to go out, 'tell me how it happened that you were there just in the nick of time to help me.'

'I heard the shot', he replied with an embarrassed air, 'and

I came out at once, fearing that something had happened to you.'

He left me hastily, after he had once again sworn me to secrecy.

In the morning a surgeon came to see me, sent no doubt by Don Ottavio. He prescribed a poultice, but asked no questions as to what had given a tinge of violets to my lily-white skin. People are very discreet in Rome, and I decided to conform with the customs of the country.

Several days passed by without my being able to talk freely with Don Ottavio. He was preoccupied and even gloomier than usual; besides, he seemed to be trying to avoid my questions. During the rare moments that I was alone with him he did not say a word about the strange inhabitants of the Viccolo di Madama Lucrezia. The day fixed for the ceremony of his ordination was drawing near, and I attributed his melancholy to his repugnance for the profession he was being forced to adopt.

For my part, I was preparing to leave Rome for Florence. When I announced my departure to the Marchesa Aldo-brandi, Don Ottavio made some excuse to take me up to his room. There he took both my hands in his.

'My dear friend,' he said, 'if you will not grant me the favour I am going to ask of you I shall certainly blow out my brains, for I see no other way out of my difficulties. I have made up my mind never to wear the wretched dress they want me to adopt. I want to escape from this country. What I am asking you to do is to take me with you, passing me off as your servant; a few words added to your passport will be enough to make my flight possible.'

At first I tried to dissuade him from his plan by speaking of the grief it would cause his mother; but, finding that his mind was made up, I ended by promising to take him with me, and to have my passport altered accordingly.

'That is not all', he said. 'My departure still depends on the success of an enterprise in which I am engaged. You intend to leave the day after tomorrow; by then I may have succeeded, and in that case I shall be completely at your service.'

'Are you mad enough', I asked uneasily, 'to have got yourself involved in some conspiracy?'

'No', he replied; 'the matter is not of such grave importance as the fate of my country, but grave enough for my life and happiness to depend on the success of my undertaking. I cannot tell you any more now. In a couple of days you shall know everything.'

I was beginning to get used to mysteries, so I resigned myself to yet another. It was arranged that we should start at three o'clock in the morning, and that we should not break our journey until we had reached Tuscan territory.

As I knew it would be useless to go to bed with such an early start in prospect, I employed the last evening of my stay in Rome in paying calls at all the houses where I had been received. I went to take leave of the Marchesa, and for form's sake I shook hands ceremoniously with her son. I felt his hand tremble in mine.

'At this moment my life is in the balance', he whispered. 'You will find a letter at your hotel from me. If I am not with you punctually at three o'clock, don't wait for me.'

I was struck by the alteration in his features, but I attributed it to a very natural emotion on his part at leaving his family, possibly for ever.

It was about one o'clock when I returned to my lodgings. I decided to walk along the Viccolo di Madama Lucrezia once more. Something white was hanging from the window which had been the scene of two such different apparitions. I approached it cautiously and saw that it was a knotted rope. Was it an invitation to go and take leave of the Signora? It looked like it, and the temptation was powerful. I did not yield to it, however, remembering my promise to Don Ottavio, and also, it must be admitted, the unpleasant reception I had brought on myself a few days before by an act which had been nothing like as bold.

I continued on my way, but slowly, for I was sorry to lose

the last opportunity of penetrating the mysteries of No. 13.
I turned my head at each step that I took, expecting every
time to see some human form climbing or descending the
rope. Nothing appeared, and at last I reached the far end of
the street which led into the Corso.

'Farewell, Madama Lucrezia', I said, and I took off my
hat to the house which I could still see. 'Find someone else,
I beg you, to carry out your revenge on the jealous lover
who keeps you imprisoned there.'

It was striking two o'clock when I entered my hotel. A
carriage loaded with luggage stood waiting in the yard. One
of the hotel waiters handed me a letter; it was from Don
Ottavio, and, as it seemed a long one, I thought that I had
better take it up to my room to read it. I asked the waiter to
light me upstairs.

'Monsieur,' he said, 'your servant, whom you told us was
going to travel with you . . .'

'Well? Has he come?'

'No, Monsieur. . . .'

'He is at the posting-station; he will come with the
horses.'

'Monsieur, a lady came a little while ago and asked to
speak to your servant. She absolutely insisted on going up
to your room, Monsieur, and told me to tell your servant as
soon as he came that Madama Lucrezia was in your room.'

'In my room!' I cried, clutching the banister rail.

'Yes, Monsieur; and it looks as if she is going too, for she
gave me a small box to put in the boot.'

My heart started pounding wildly, and I was seized by a
strange mixture of superstitious terror and curiosity. I went
up the stairs step by step. When we reached the first floor
(my room was on the second), the waiter, who was in front
of me, tripped, and the candle which he was holding in his
hand fell and went out. He apologized profusely, and went
downstairs to relight it. In the meantime I went on upstairs.

I had my hand on the key of my room, but I hesitated.

What fresh vision was I going to see? More than once, in the darkness, the story of the bleeding nun had returned to me. Was I possessed by a demon, like Don Alonso? The waiter seemed a terribly long time in coming.

I opened the door. To my relief there was a light in my bedroom. I rapidly crossed the little sitting-room which came first, and a single glance was enough to show me that no one was in my bedroom; but immediately I heard some light footsteps behind me, and the rustle of a skirt. I believe that my hair stood on end as I turned round suddenly.

A woman dressed in white, her head covered with a black mantilla, came towards me with outstretched arms.

'Here you are at last, my beloved!' she cried, seizing my hands.

Hers were as cold as ice, and her features were as pale as death. I started back against the wall.

'Holy Mother! It is not he . . . ! Oh, are you Don Ottavio's friend?'

At that name everything became clear. In spite of her pallor the young lady did not look at all like a ghost; she lowered her eyes, a thing ghosts never do, and held her hands clasped in a modest attitude over her waist, which made me think that my friend Don Ottavio was not so much of a politician as I had imagined. In short, it was high time to take Lucrezia away; and, unfortunately, the role of confidant was the only one entrusted to me in this adventure.

A moment later, Don Ottavio arrived in disguise. The horses were brought along and we set off. Lucrezia had no passport; but a woman, especially a pretty one, arouses no suspicions. One gendarme, however, raised difficulties. I told him that he was a fine fellow, and must have served under the great Napoleon. He acknowledged the fact, and I offered him a portrait of that great man on a gold chain, telling him that it was my habit to travel with an *amica* to keep me company; and that, as I frequently changed them, I did not think it any use putting their names on my passport.

'This one', I added, 'is taking me to the next town. I have been told that I shall find others there who are just as good.'

'You would do wrong to change her', said the gendarme, as he respectfully shut the carriage door.

To tell you the truth, that rascal Don Ottavio had made the acquaintance of that lovely young lady, the sister of a certain wealthy farmer called Vanozzi, who had a bad name as something of a liberal and a notorious smuggler. Don Ottavio knew very well that, even if his family had not intended him for the Church, they would never have agreed to let him marry a girl so much lower in social position than himself.

Love is ingenious. The Abbé Negroni's pupil succeeded in embarking on a secret correspondence with his beloved. Every night he escaped from the Aldobrandi palace, and, as it would have been unsafe to scale the walls of Vanozzi's house, the two lovers used to meet in Madama Lucrezia's house, protected by its ill-repute. A little door hidden by a fig tree communicated between the two gardens. Young and in love, Lucrezia and Ottavio did not complain of the paucity of the furniture, which consisted, as I think I have already mentioned, of an old leather arm-chair.

One night, when waiting for Don Ottavio, Lucrezia mistook me for him, and gave me the present which I received in his place. There was certainly some resemblance between Don Ottavio's face and figure and my own, and certain scandal-mongers who had known my father in Rome, maintained that there were reasons for this likeness. In the course of time the brother discovered their meetings; but his threats did not make Lucrezia reveal her seducer's name. You know how he took his revenge and how I nearly paid for the two lovers. There is no need to tell you how they made their escape.

To conclude, we all three arrived at Florence. Don Ottavio married Lucrezia, and they left immediately for Paris. My father gave him as warm a welcome as I had received at the hands of the Marchesa. He took it upon himself to bring about a reconciliation, and after a good deal of trouble he succeeded. The Marchesa Aldobrandi was opportunely taken with the Maremma fever and died. Ottavio inherited his title and fortune, and I became godfather to his firstborn.

27 April 1846

The Blue Chamber

To Madame de la Rhune

A YOUNG man was walking up and down the entrance-hall of a railway station, in a state of agitation. He was wearing blue spectacles, and, although he did not have a cold, he kept putting his handkerchief to his nose. He had a little black bag in his left hand which, as I learnt later, contained a silk dressing-gown and a pair of Turkish pantaloons.

Every now and again he went to the door and looked into the street, then he took out his watch and consulted the station clock. The train did not leave for another hour; but there are people who are always afraid of being late. This train was not for people in a great hurry; there were few first-class carriages on it. It was not an hour at which stockbrokers could set off, after business was finished, to go to their country houses for dinner. When travellers began to appear, a Parisian would have recognized from their appearance that they were either farmers or small suburban tradesmen. All the same, every time a woman came into the station, or a carriage drew up at the door, the heart of the young man with the blue spectacles swelled up like a balloon, his knees trembled, his bag almost fell from his hands and his glasses off his nose, where, it may be mentioned in passing, they were perched askew.

His agitation increased when, after a long wait, a woman appeared by a side door, from precisely the direction in which he had not kept a constant look-out. She was dressed in black with a thick veil over her face, and she held a brown morocco bag in her hand, containing, as I subsequently discovered, a wonderful dressing-gown and a pair of blue satin slippers. The woman and the young man advanced towards each other, looking to right and left, but never in front of them. They came up to one another, touched hands, and stood for a few moments without speaking a word, trembling and gasping, a prey to one of those intense emotions for which I would exchange a hundred years of a philosopher's life.

'Léon,' said the young woman, when she had recovered the power to speak (I had forgotten to mention that she was young and pretty), 'Léon, how happy I am! I should never have recognized you with those blue spectacles.'

'How happy I am!' said Léon. 'I should never have known you under that black veil.'

'How happy I am!' she repeated. 'Let's be quick and take our seats; suppose the train were to start without us ... !' (And she squeezed his arm tightly.) 'No one suspects anything. I am now with Clara and her husband, on the way to their country house, where *tomorrow* I must say good-bye to her. ... And', she added, laughing and lowering her head, 'she left an hour ago; and tomorrow ... after spending the *last evening* with her ... (again she pressed his arm), tomorrow, in the morning, she will leave me at the station, where I shall meet Ursule, whom I sent on ahead to my aunt's. ... Oh, I've arranged everything. Let's take our tickets. ... They can't possibly guess who we are. Oh, suppose they ask for our names at the inn? I've forgotten already. ...'

'Monsieur and Madame Duru.'

'Oh, no! Not Duru. There was a shoemaker called that at the pension.'

'Dumont, then?'

'Daumont.'

'Very well. But no one will ask us.'

The bell rang, the door of the waiting-room opened, and the young woman, still carefully veiled, hurriedly climbed into a carriage with her youthful companion. The bell rang a second time, and the door of their compartment was closed.

'We are alone!' they exclaimed delightedly.

P

But, almost at the same moment, a man of about fifty, dressed completely in black, with a grave and bored expression, entered the carriage and settled himself in a corner. The engine whistled, and the train began to move. The two young people drew as far away as they could from their unwelcome neighbour and began to whisper in English as an additional precaution.

'Monsieur,' said the other traveller, in the same tongue, and with a much purer English accent, 'if you have any secrets to tell each other, you had better not tell them in English before me, for I am an Englishman. I am extremely sorry to annoy you; but there was a man by himself in the other compartment, and I make it a rule never to travel alone with another man. . . . He had the face of a scoundrel, and this might have tempted him.'

He pointed to his travelling-bag, which he had thrown on the cushion opposite him.

'Besides, I shall read if I don't go to sleep.'

And, indeed, he did make a gallant effort to sleep. He opened his bag, took out a comfortable cap, put it on his head, and kept his eyes shut for a few minutes then he reopened them with a gesture of impatience and looked in his bag for his spectacles, then for a Greek book. At last he settled down to read, with an air of concentration. To get his book out of the bag he had to displace a good many things piled together haphazardly. Among others, he drew out of the depths of the bag a large bundle of Bank of England notes, placed it on the seat opposite him, and, before putting it back in the bag, showed it to the young man and asked him if it would be possible for him to change bank-notes at N——.

'Probably, as it is on the way to England.'

N—— was the place to which the two young people were going. There is a pleasant little hotel at N——, where people seldom stop except on Saturday nights. It is said that the rooms are good, but that the host and his staff are not far enough away from Paris to indulge in this provincial vice. The young man whom I have already called by the name of Léon had been to reconnoitre this hotel some time previously, without his blue spectacles, and on the report he had given of it, his companion had shown a desire to visit it.

She was, moreover, in such a state of mind that day, that the walls of a prison would have seemed delightful to her, if she had been shut up inside them with Léon.

In the meantime the train travelled on; the Englishman read his Greek book, without looking at his companions, who talked together in that low tone that only lovers can hear. Perhaps I shall not astonish my readers when I tell them that these two were lovers in the fullest acceptance of the term, and what was deplorable, they were not married, and there were reasons which prevented them from being married.

They arrived at N——, and the Englishman got out first. While Léon was helping his friend to get down from the carriage without showing her legs, a man jumped on to the platform from the next compartment. He was pale, even sallow; his eyes were sunken and bloodshot, and his beard unkempt, a sign by which great criminals are often detected. His clothes were clean, but worn almost threadbare. His frock-coat, once black, but now grey at the back and at the elbows, was buttoned up to his chin, probably to hide an even shabbier waistcoat. He went up to the Englishman and in a deferential voice said:

'Uncle!'

'Leave me alone, you wretch!' cried the Englishman, his eyes flashing with anger; and he took a step forward to leave the station.

'Don't drive me to despair', replied the other, in a piteous yet at the same time almost menacing tone of voice.

'Will you be good enough to look after my bag for a moment?' said the old Englishman, throwing his travelling-bag at Léon's feet.

He then took the man who had accosted him by the arm

and led, or rather pushed him into a corner, where he hoped they would not be overheard, and there he talked to him for a while in what seemed a very harsh manner. He then drew some papers from his pocket, crumpled them up, and thrust them into the hand of the man who had called him uncle. The latter took the papers without offering any thanks, and almost immediately walked away and disappeared.

As there is only one hotel at N—— it was not surprising that, a few minutes later, all the characters of this true story came together again there. In France any traveller who has the good fortune to have a well-dressed woman on his arm is certain to obtain the best room in any hotel, with the result that we are reputed to be the politest nation in Europe.

If the bedroom which was assigned to Léon was the best, it would be rash to conclude that it was perfect. There was a big walnut bedstead, with chintz curtains on which was printed in violet the legendary story of Pyramis and Thisbe. The walls were covered with paper representing a view of Naples and a multitude of people; unfortunately, idle and impertinent travellers had added moustaches and pipes to all the figures, both male and female, and a good many stupid things in verse and prose had been pencilled on the sky and the ocean. On this background there hung several engravings: *Louis Philippe taking the Oath of Loyalty to the Charter of 1830; The First Meeting between Julie and Saint-Preux*; *Waiting for Happiness,* and *Regrets,* after Monsieur Dubuffe. This room was called the Blue Chamber, because the two arm-chairs to the left and right of the fireplace were upholstered in Utrecht velvet of that colour; but for a good many years they had been draped in loose covers of grey calico edged with red braid.

While the hotel maids fussed around the newly arrived lady and offered her their services, Léon, who, although in love, was not devoid of common sense, went to the kitchen to order dinner. It took all his eloquence and a few bribes to extract the promise of a dinner served in his room. Great was his dismay when he learnt that in the principal dining-room, which was next to his room, the officers of the 3rd Hussars, who were about to relieve the officers of the 3rd Chasseurs at N——, were going to join them that very day in a farewell dinner which would be a lively affair. The host swore by all the gods that, apart from the gaiety which was natural to every French soldier, the officers of the Hussars and the Chasseurs were known throughout the town for their quiet, discreet behaviour, and that their proximity would not inconvenience Madame in the least, since the officers were in the habit of leaving the table before midnight.

As Léon was returning to the Blue Chamber, only slightly reassured, he noticed that the Englishman had been given the other room next to his. The door was open, and the Englishman was sitting at a table on which there were a glass and a bottle. He was looking at the ceiling with profound attention, as if he were counting the flies walking on it.

'What does it matter who my neighbours are?' Léon said to himself. 'The Englishman will soon be tipsy, and the Hussars will leave before midnight.'

On entering the Blue Chamber the first thing he did was to make sure that the communicating doors were securely locked, and that they had bolts on them. There were double doors on the Englishman's side, and the walls were thick. The partition was thinner on the Hussars' side, but the door had a lock and a bolt. After all, this was a more effectual barrier to curiosity than the blinds of a carriage, and how many people think that they are cut off from the world in a hackney carriage!

Certainly the richest imagination cannot picture a more complete state of happiness than that of two young lovers, who, after waiting a long time, find themselves alone and far from jealous and prying eyes, able to relate to each other at leisure their past sufferings and to taste the delights of a perfect reunion. But the Devil always finds a way to pour his drop of wormwood into the cup of happiness.

Johnson has written—repeating the dictum of a Greek writer—that no man can say: 'Today I shall be happy'. This truth, recognized at a very remote period by the greatest philosophers, is still ignored by a certain number of mortals, and especially by most lovers.

While eating a rather poor dinner in the Blue Chamber, consisting of a few dishes filched from the Hussars' and Chasseurs' banquet, Léon and his mistress were greatly disturbed by the conversation in which the gentlemen in the next room were engaged. This was a conversation totally unconnected with strategy and tactics, and which I shall take good care not to repeat.

It was a succession of comical stories, nearly all of them broad, accompanied by roars of laughter in which it was often difficult for our lovers not to join. Léon's mistress was no prude; but there are some things one prefers not to hear, particularly when one is alone with the man one loves. The situation became more and more embarrassing, and when the officers were about to be served with dessert, Léon felt compelled to go downstairs to beg the host to tell those gentlemen that there was a sick woman in the next room, and to ask them as a matter of courtesy to make a little less noise.

As often happens with regimental dinners, the landlord was rushed off his feet, and did not know which way to turn. Just as Léon was giving him his message for the officers, a waiter asked him for some champagne for the Hussars, and a maidservant for some port for the Englishman.

'I told him there was none', she added.

'You're a fool. I've every kind of wine. I'll give him some port! Bring me the bottle of rum, a bottle of cheap wine, and a decanter of brandy.'

After concocting some port in a hurry, the host went into the main dining-room to execute Léon's commission, which at first raised a storm of protest.

Then a deep voice, which dominated all the others, asked

what sort of a woman their neighbour was. There was a brief silence before the host replied.:

'Really, gentlemen, I don't know what to say to you. She's very charming and very shy. Marie-Jeanne says she has a wedding-ring on her finger. She might be a bride who has come here on her honeymoon, as some do.'

'A bride?' exclaimed forty voices. 'She must come and have a drink with us! We'll drink her health and teach the husband his conjugal duties.'

At these words there was a great jingling of spurs, and our lovers trembled, fearing that their room was about to be taken by storm.

But suddenly a voice was raised which stopped the movement. It obviously belonged to a commanding officer. He reproached the officers with their want of politeness, and ordered them to sit down again and to talk decently, without shouting. Then he added a few words in a voice too low to be heard in the Blue Chamber. He was listened to with deference, but not without exciting a certain amount of restrained hilarity. From that moment there was comparative quiet from the officers' room; and our lovers, blessing the salutary power of discipline, began to talk together with more freedom. . . . But after so much trouble it was some time before they could recapture those tender emotions which anxiety, the worries of travelling, and, above all, the coarse merriment of the neighbours, had so greatly disturbed. This is not very difficult to do, however, at their age, and they had soon forgotten all the unpleasant aspects of their amorous expedition in order to give their minds entirely to its more important consequences.

They thought that peace had been made with the Hussars. Alas, it was only a truce. Just as they were least expecting it, when they were a thousand leagues away from this sublunary world, twenty-four trumpets, supported by a few trombones, sounded that tune well known to French soldiers: *Victory is Ours*! How could anyone resist such an onslaught? The poor lovers were greatly to be pitied.

No, they were not so much to be pitied, for at last the officers left the dining-room, filing past the door of the Blue Chamber with a great clattering of spurs and sabres, and shouting one after the other:

'Good night to the bride!'

Then silence fell. No, I am mistaken; the Englishman came out into the passage and called out:

'Waiter! Bring me another bottle of the same port.'

Quiet was restored in the hotel at N——. The night was fine and the moon full. From time immemorial, lovers have been delighted in gazing at our satellite. Léon and his lover opened their window, which looked out on a little garden, and breathed in the fresh air which was filled with the scent from a bower of clematis.

They did not stay at the window for long, however. A man was strolling in the garden, his head bowed, his arms folded, and a cigar in his mouth. Léon thought that he recognized the nephew of the Englishman who was so fond of good port.

*　　　*　　　*

I dislike useless details, and besides, I do not feel called upon to tell the reader things he can readily imagine, nor to relate, hour by hour, all that happened in the hotel at N——. I will therefore merely say that the candle which burned on the mantelpiece of the Blue Chamber was more than half consumed when a strange sound came from the Englishman's room, in which there had been silence until then; it was like the fall of a heavy body. To this noise was added a sort of cracking sound, quite as odd, followed by a smothered cry and several inarticulate words like an oath. The two young occupants of the Blue Chamber shuddered. Perhaps they had been suddenly awakened by it. The noise had made a sinister impression on them both, which they could not explain to themselves.

'Our friend the Englishman is dreaming', said Léon, making an effort to smile.

But he was trying to reassure his companion, and he shivered involuntarily. Two or three minutes later a door in the corridor was opened cautiously, as it seemed, and then closed very quietly. They heard someone walking with a slow, unsteady gait and, by all appearances, trying to make no noise.

'What a confounded inn!' exclaimed Léon.

'Ah, it's a paradise!' replied the young woman, letting her head fall on Léon's shoulder. 'I'm so sleepy!'

She sighed, and fell asleep again almost immediately.

A famous moralist has said that men are never garrulous when they have all that their hearts desire. It is not surprising, therefore, that Léon made no attempt to renew the conversation or to discourse upon the noises in the hotel at N——. Nevertheless, he was intrigued by them, and his imagination connected them with various circumstances to which in another mood he would have paid no attention. The evil face of the Englishman's nephew returned to his memory. There had been hatred in the look that he had thrown at his uncle even while he had been speaking humbly to him, doubtless because he had been asking him for money.

What could be easier than for a man who was still young and strong, and desperate too, to climb from the garden to the window of the next room? Moreover, he was staying at the hotel, since he had been strolling in the garden after dark. Perhaps . . . probably even . . . undoubtedly, he knew that his uncle's black bag contained a thick bundle of bank-notes. . . . And that dull blow, like the blow of a club on a bald head! . . . That stifled cry! . . . That fearful oath! And those footsteps afterwards! That nephew looked like a murderer. . . . But people don't commit murders in a hotel full of officers. Surely the Englishman, like a wise man, had locked himself in, especially knowing that the scoundrel was in the vicinity. . . . He obviously mistrusted him, since he had not wished to accost him with his bag in his hand. . . . But why indulge in such hideous thoughts when one is so happy?

This is what Léon said to himself. In the midst of his thoughts, which I will refrain from analysing at greater length, and which passed through his mind almost as haphazardly as the visions in a dream, he kept his eyes fixed mechanically on the communicating door between the Blue Chamber and the Englishman's room.

In France, doors fit badly. Between this one and the floor there was a gap of nearly an inch. Suddenly, in this space, which was hardly lighted by the reflection from the polished floor, there appeared something blackish and flat, like a knife blade, for the edge, caught by the candlelight, showed a thin line which shone brightly. It moved slowly in the direction of a little blue satin slipper, which had been carelessly thrown close to this door. Was it some insect like a centipede . . . ? No, it was no insect. It had no definite shape. . . . Two or three brown streaks, each with its line of light at the edges, had come into the room. Their pace quickened, for the floor sloped. . . . They moved rapidly and soon touched the little slipper. There could no longer be any doubt! It was a liquid, and that liquid, the colour of which could now be distinctly seen in the candlelight, was blood! While Léon, paralysed with horror, gazed at these frightful streams, the young woman slept on peacefully, her regular breathing warming her lover's neck and shoulder.

The care which Léon had taken in ordering the dinner on their arrival at the hotel offered adequate proof that he had a level head, a high degree of intelligence, and the capacity to look ahead. In this emergency he did not belie the characteristics he had already displayed. He did not stir a muscle, and his whole mind was concentrated on the problem of coming to a decision in face of the frightful disaster which threatened him.

I imagine that most of my readers, and above all my lady readers, full of heroic sentiments, will criticize Léon for remaining motionless in these circumstances. They will tell me that he ought to have rushed to the Englishman's room and arrested the murderer, or, at least, to have rung his bell and awakened the staff of the hotel. To this I would reply that, in the first place, the bells in French inns are only ornaments, and their ropes do not correspond to any metallic apparatus. I would add respectfully, but firmly, that, if it is deplorable to leave an Englishman to die in the next room, it is not praiseworthy to sacrifice for his sake a woman who is sleeping with her head on your shoulder. What would have happened if Léon had made an uproar and roused the hotel? The police, the public prosecutor, and his clerk would have come at once. These gentlemen are by profession so curious, that, before asking him what he had seen or heard, they would have asked him first of all:

'What is your name? Where are your papers? And what about Madame? What were you doing together in the Blue Chamber? You will have to appear at the Assizes to testify that on such a date, of such a month, at such an hour of the night, you were witnesses of such an incident.'

Now it was precisely this thought, of the public prosecutor and the officers of the law, which first occurred to Léon. Sometimes in life there arise questions of conscience which are difficult to solve. Is it better to allow an unknown traveller to have his throat cut, or to disgrace and lose the woman one loves?

It is unpleasant to be confronted with such a problem. I defy the cleverest person to solve it.

Léon did then what many men would probably have done in his place: he did not budge.

He remained as if hypnotized for a long time, with his eyes fixed on the blue slipper and the little red stream which touched it, while a cold sweat moistened his temples, and his heart beat in his breast as if it would burst.

A host of thoughts and strange and horrible fancies haunted him, and an inner voice kept crying out to him: 'In an hour all will be known, and it is your own fault!' Nevertheless, by dint of repeating to oneself: 'What the devil am I to do?' one ends up by perceiving a few rays of hope.

'If we left this accursed hotel', he said to himself at last, 'before the discovery of what has happened in the next room, perhaps we could escape without trace. No one knows us here. I have only been seen in blue spectacles, and she has only been seen in a veil. We are only a short distance from the station, and in an hour we should be far away from N——.'

Then, as he had studied the time-table at great length in order to plan his journey, he recollected that a train for Paris left at eight o'clock. Soon afterwards they would be lost in the vastness of that city, where so many guilty persons are concealed. Who could discover two innocent people there? But would not someone go into the Englishman's room before eight o'clock? That was the vital question.

Quite convinced that there was no other course open to him, he made a desperate effort to shake off the torpor which had taken possession of him for so long; but at the first movement he made, his young companion woke up and kissed him half consciously. At the touch of his icy cheek she gave a little cry.

'What is the matter?' she asked him anxiously. 'Your forehead is as cold as marble.'

'It's nothing', he replied in a voice which belied his words. 'I heard a noise in the next room. . . .'

He freed himself from her arms, and then moved the blue slipper and put an arm-chair in front of the communicating door so as to hide the dreadful liquid from his mistress's eyes. It had stopped flowing, and had now collected into quite a big pool on the floor. Then he half opened the door which led to the passage, and listened attentively. He even ventured to go up to the Englishman's door, which was closed. There was already some movement in the hotel, for day was breaking. The stable-boys were grooming the horses in the yard, and an officer came downstairs from the second storey, clinking his spurs. He was on his way to supervise that interesting operation, more agreeable to horses than to men, which is technically known as *la botte.*[1]

Léon went back into the Blue Chamber, and, with every precaution that love could invent, with the help of much circumlocution and many euphemisms, he explained the situation to his mistress.

It was dangerous to stay and dangerous to leave too precipitately; still more dangerous to wait at the hotel until the catastrophe in the next room was discovered.

There is no need to describe the terror caused by this explanation, the tears which followed it, or the mad suggestions which were made; or how many times the two unhappy young people flung themselves into each other's arms, saying: 'Forgive me! forgive me!' Each considered himself the more to blame. They vowed to die together, for the young woman had no doubt that the law would find them guilty of the murder of the Englishman, and as they were not sure that they would be allowed to embrace each other again on the scaffold, they did it now to suffocation, and vied with each other in shedding tears. At last, after talking a great deal of nonsense and exchanging a great many tender and harrowing words, they decided, in the midst of a thousand kisses, that the plan thought out by Léon, namely, to leave by the eight o'clock train, was really the only practical one and the best to follow. But there were still two mortal hours to get through. At each footstep in the corridor they trembled in every limb. Each creak of boots seemed to proclaim the arrival of the public prosecutor.

Their packing was done in a flash. The young woman wanted to burn the blue slipper in the fireplace; but Léon picked it up and, after wiping it on the bedside rug, he kissed it and put it in his pocket. He was astonished to find that it smelt of vanilla, though his mistress's perfume was *Bouquet de l'Impératrice Eugénie.*

Everybody in the hotel was now awake. They could hear waiters laughing, servant-girls singing at their work, and

---

[1] The horses' feed. (Translator's note.)

soldiers brushing their officers' clothes. Seven o'clock had just struck. Léon wanted to make his mistress drink a cup of coffee, but she declared that her throat was so constricted that she should die if she tried to drink anything.

Léon, armed with his blue spectacles, went down to pay the bill. The host begged his pardon for the noise that had been made; he could not understand it, for the officers were always so quiet! Léon assured him that he had heard nothing, and that he had slept profoundly.

'I don't think your neighbour on the other side can have disturbed you', continued the landlord. 'He doesn't make much noise. I bet he's still fast asleep.'

Léon leant hard against the desk to keep from falling, and the young woman, who had insisted on accompanying him, clutched his arm and tightened the veil over her face.

'He's an English lord', added the pitiless host. 'He always wants the best of everything. Oh, he's a good sort. But the English aren't all like him. There was one here who's a regular skinflint. He thought everything too dear: his room, his dinner. He wanted me to take a five-pound Bank of England note in settlement of his bill for one hundred and eighty-five francs. . . . I only hope it's a good one! Why, Monsieur, perhaps you'll know, for I've heard you talking English with Madame. . . . Is it a good one?'

With these words he showed Léon a five-pound banknote. On one of the corners there was a little red stain which Léon promptly explained to himself.

'I think it's perfectly good', he said in a choking voice.

'Oh, you've plenty of time', the host went on; 'the train isn't due here until eight o'clock, and it's always late. Won't you sit down, Madame? You look rather tired.'

At that moment a fat servant-girl came in.

'Some hot water, quick,' she said, 'for milord's tea. Give me a sponge too. He's broken his bottle of port and the whole room is flooded.'

At these words Léon dropped into a chair, and his companion did the same. An intense desire to laugh took hold of them both, and they had the greatest difficulty in restraining themselves. The young woman squeezed her lover's hand joyfully.

'I think we'll wait to take the two o'clock train', Léon said to the landlord. 'Let us have a good meal at midday.'

Biarritz, September 1866

Djoumane

On 21 May 18—, we were returning to Tlemcen. The expedition had been a successful one; we were bringing back oxen, sheep, goats, prisoners, and hostages.

After thirty-seven days of campaign, or rather of incessant pursuit, our horses were thin and lean-ribbed, but their eyes were still bright and full of fire; not one of them was saddle-galled. Our men, bronzed by the sun, with long hair, dirty cross-belts, and threadbare tunics, presented that appearance of indifference to danger and hardship which characterizes the true soldier.

What general would not have chosen our light cavalry for a battle-charge rather than the smartest of squadrons all decked out in new uniforms?

Since morning I had been thinking of all the little pleasures that awaited me.

Now I would sleep in my iron bedstead, after having slept for thirty-seven nights on a rectangle of oilcloth. I would sit on a chair to eat my dinner, and have as much soft bread and salt as I liked. Next I wondered whether Mademoiselle Concha would be wearing a pomegranate flower or a jasmine blossom in her hair, and if she had kept the vows made when I had left; but, faithful or inconstant, I knew she could reckon on the great depth of tenderness that a man brings home from the desert. There was no one in our squadron who had not made plans for the evening.

The colonel received us in a very fatherly manner, and even told us he was pleased with us; then he took our commanding officer aside and for five minutes, in a low voice, gave him some news which was not particularly pleasant, so far as we could judge from their expressions.

We watched the movements of the colonel's mustachios,

which rose up to his eyebrows, while the commanding officer's drooped piteously and limply almost to his chest. A young trooper, whom I pretended not to hear, maintained that the commanding officer's nose was visibly lengthening; but soon ours lengthened too, when he came and said to us: 'Go and feed the horses, and be ready to set off at sunset. The officers will dine with the colonel at five o'clock, in field uniform, and ride off after coffee. . . . You aren't by any chance displeased at this, are you, gentlemen . . . ?'

We made no reply and saluted in silence, inwardly sending him to all the devils, and the colonel with him.

We had very little time in which to make our modest preparations. I hurriedly changed and, when I had done this, took care not to sit in my easy-chair for fear I should fall asleep.

At five o'clock I went to the colonel's. He lived in a large Moorish house. I found the courtyard full of people, both Frenchmen and natives, crowding round a band of pilgrims or mountebanks who had come from the south.

An old man was directing the performance; he was as ugly as a monkey and half naked under a burnous which was full of holes. His skin was the colour of a chocolate sorbet; he was tattooed all over; his hair was frizzy and so bushy that from a distance one might have thought he had a bearskin cap on his head; and his beard was white and bristly. He was reputed to be a great saint and a great wizard.

In front of him an orchestra consisting of two flautists and three drummers was making an infernal din, worthy of the performance about to be presented. He said that he had received complete power over demons and wild beasts from a famous marabout, and, after some compliments addressed to the colonel and the audience, he launched himself into a sort of prayer or incantation, accompanied by his orchestra, while the actors jumped about and danced to his command, spinning on one foot, and beating their breasts with their fists.

Meanwhile the drums and flutes played faster and faster.

Q

When exhaustion and giddiness had fuddled what few brains these people had, the chief sorcerer took some scorpions and serpents out of some baskets around him, and, after showing that they were full of life, he threw them to these fellows, who fell upon them like dogs on a bone and tore them to pieces with their teeth, if you please.

We looked down at this extraordinary spectacle from a high gallery; no doubt the colonel was treating us to it to give us a good appetite for our dinner. As for myself, I turned my eyes away from these rogues, who disgusted me, and amused myself by looking at a pretty girl of thirteen or fourteen who was threading her way through the crowd to get nearer to the performance.

She had the most beautiful eyes imaginable, and her hair fell on her shoulders in fine tresses; these ended in small pieces of silver, which made a tinkling sound as she moved her head gracefully about. She was dressed with more taste than most of the girls of that country; she had a gold silk kerchief on her head, a tunic of embroidered velvet, and short pantaloons of blue satin, showing her bare legs encircled with silver anklets. There was no veil over her face. Was she a Jewess or a heathen, or did she perhaps belong to those wandering tribes of unknown origin who never trouble themselves with religious prejudices?

While I was following her every movement with so much interest she had reached the first row of the circle, where the fanatics were giving their performance.

While she was trying to get still nearer she knocked over a narrow-bottomed basket which had not been opened. Almost at the same time the sorcerer and the child both uttered a terrible cry, and there was a great commotion in the ring, everyone recoiling in horror.

A very big snake had just escaped from the basket and the little girl had trodden on it. In an instant the reptile had wound itself round her leg and I saw a few drops of blood trickle under the ring which she wore round her ankle. She fell down backwards, crying and grinding her teeth, and white foam flecked her lips while she rolled in the dust.

'Run, doctor!' I cried to our surgeon-major; 'for God's sake save the poor child.'

'Greenhorn!' the major replied, shrugging his shoulders. 'Don't you see that it's part of the programme? Besides, my job is cutting off your arms and legs. It's up to my colleague down there to cure girls who are bitten by snakes.'

In the meantime the old wizard had run up, and the first thing he did was to recapture the snake.

'Djoumane! Djoumane!' he said to it in a tone of friendly reproach. The snake uncoiled itself, abandoned its prey, and started to crawl away. The sorcerer nimbly seized it by the end of its tail, and holding it at arm's length, he went round the circle exhibiting the reptile, which writhed and twisted without being able to stand erect.

You probably know that a snake held by its tail does not know what to do with itself. It can only raise itself a quarter of its length, and cannot therefore bite the hand which has seized it.

The next minute the snake was put back in its basket and the lid firmly fastened down. The magician then turned his attention to the little girl, who was still shrieking and kicking about. He put a pinch of white powder, which he took from his belt, on the wound, and whispered an incantation in the child's ear, with immediate effect. The convulsions ceased; the little girl wiped her mouth, picked up her silk kerchief, shook the dust off it, put it on her head again, stood up, and soon afterwards left the courtyard.

A little later she came up to our gallery to collect money, and we fastened a great many fifty-centime coins on her forehead and shoulders.

This concluded the performance, and we sat down to dinner.

I was very hungry and was preparing to do justice to a splendid broiled eel, when our doctor, who was sitting next to me, said that he recognized the snake we had been watching. That made it quite impossible for me to eat a single mouthful.

After making great fun of my fastidiousness the doctor annexed my share of the eel, and assured me that snake tasted delicious.

'Those brutes you saw just now', he said to me, 'are connoisseurs. They live in caves with their snakes like troglodytes; their girls are pretty—witness the little girl in the blue pantaloons. No one knows what their religion is, but they're a cunning lot, and I should like to meet their sheik.'

We learnt during the dinner why we were taking the field again. Sidi-Lala, hotly pursued by Colonel R——, was trying to reach the mountains of Morocco.

There was a choice of two routes; one to the south of Tlemcen, fording the Moulaia at the only place not rendered inaccessible by rocks; the other by the plain, to the north of our cantonment, where he would be confronted by our colonel and the bulk of the regiment.

Our squadron had orders to stop him at the river crossing if he attempted it, but this was scarcely likely.

I should add that the Moulaia flows between two walls of rock, and there is only a single point, like a kind of narrow breach, where horses can ford it. I knew the place well, and I couldn't understand why a blockhouse had not yet been built there. The fact remains that the colonel had every chance of encountering the enemy, and we of making a useless journey.

Before we had finished dinner several orderlies from the Maghzen had brought dispatches from Colonel R——. The enemy had made a stand, and seemed to want to fight. They had lost time. Colonel R——'s infantry was going to come up and rout them.

But which way would they flee? We had no idea, and had to keep watch for him along both routes. I make no mention of a final course which he could take, namely, to flee into the desert, for there his herds and his men would soon die of hunger and thirst. We agreed upon some signals with which to inform one another of the enemy's movements.

Three cannon-shots fired at Tlemcen would tell us that Sidi-Lala was visible in the plain, and we for our part would carry rockets with us in case we had to call for reinforcements. In all probability the enemy could not appear before daybreak, and our two columns had several hours' start.

Night had fallen by the time we mounted our horses. I was in command of the advance platoon. I felt tired and cold; I put on my cloak, turned up the collar, thrust my feet into my stirrups and jogged quietly along on my mare, listening absent-mindedly to Sergeant Wagner's story of his love affairs, which ended unhappily with the flight of an unfaithful mistress who had run off not only with his heart, but with a silver watch and a pair of new boots also. I had heard this story before, and it appeared even longer than usual.

The moon was rising as we started on our way. The sky was clear, but a light, white mist was floating just above the ground, which looked as if it were covered with cotton wool. On this white background the moon was casting long shadows, and everything was taking on a ghostly appearance. Sometimes I thought I saw some mounted Arab sentries, but as I came nearer I found they were tamarisks in flower; sometimes I stopped short, thinking I could hear the cannon-shot signal, but Wagner told me it was the sound of a horse galloping.

We reached the ford and the commanding officer made his preparations.

The place was a wonderful defensive position, and our squadron would have been sufficient to hold a considerable force there. The other side of the river was completely deserted.

After a fairly long wait we heard the gallop of a horse, and soon an Arab came in sight mounted on a magnificent animal and riding towards us. From his straw hat crowned with ostrich feathers, and his embroidered saddle from which there hung a *gebira* decorated with coral and chased with gold flowers, we realized that he was a chief; our guide told us it was Sidi-Lala himself. He was a handsome, well-built young man, who managed his horse admirably. He put it at a gallop, threw his long gun into the air and caught it again, shouting at us unintelligible words of defiance.

The days of chivalry are over, and Wagner called for a gun to 'pick off' the marabout, as he put it; but I objected, and so that it should not be said that the French had refused to meet an Arab in single combat, I asked the commanding officer for permission to go over the ford and cross swords with Sidi-Lala. Permission was granted me, and I immediately crossed the river, while the enemy chief rode away at a trot to give himself room.

As soon as he saw I was across he rode at me with his gun aimed.

'Take care!' cried Wagner.

I have little fear of a horseman's shots, and after the tricks he had just played with it, I thought that Sidi-Lala's gun could not be in a condition to fire. Sure enough, he pulled the trigger when he was only three paces from me, but the gun missed fire as I had expected. Straight away he turned his horse round so rapidly that instead of planting my sabre in his breast I only caught his floating burnous.

But I pressed him close, keeping him always on my right and beating him back, willy-nilly, towards the steep cliffs which bordered the river. He tried in vain to turn aside: I pressed him closer and closer.

After a few minutes of frantic galloping, I suddenly saw his horse rear up and the rider draw rein with both hands. Without stopping to ask myself why he had made such a strange movement, I was on to him like a shot and planted my blade right in the middle of his back, while at the same time my horse's hoof struck his left thigh. Man and horse disappeared, and my mare and I fell after them.

Without noticing it we had reached the edge of the precipice and had hurled ourselves over it. . . . While I was still in the air—so swift is thought—I reflected that the Arab's body would break my fall. I distinctly saw beneath me a white burnous with a large red patch, and it was there that I fell, trusting to the gods.

It was not such a terrible fall as I had feared, thanks to the depth of the water; I went right in and splashed about for a moment, quite stunned, and I do not know exactly how I found myself standing in the midst of some tall reeds at the river's edge.

I knew nothing of what had become of Sidi-Lala and the horses. I was dripping and shivering in the mud, between two walls of rock. I took a few steps forward, hoping to find a place where the cliffs were less steep; but the farther I went, the more sheer and inaccessible they looked.

Suddenly I heard above my head the sound of horses' hooves and the jangling of sabres against stirrups and spurs; it was obviously our squadron. I wanted to call out, but not a sound would come out of my throat; I must have broken my ribs in my fall.

Imagine the situation I was in. I could hear our men's voices and recognize them, and I could not call them to my aid.

'If he had let me do as I wanted,' old Wagner was saying, 'he would have lived to be a colonel.'

The sound soon lessened and died away, and I heard nothing more.

Above my head there hung a thick root, and I hoped by seizing this to hoist myself up on to the bank of the river. With a desperate effort I sprang up, and ... sss! ... the root twisted and escaped from my hands with a frightful hissing. ... It was an enormous snake. ...

I fell back into the water; the snake slipped between my legs and shot into the river, where it seemed to leave a trail of fire. ...

A moment later I had regained my composure, and that shimmering light on the water had not disappeared. I finally realized that it was the reflection from a torch. About twenty yards a way, a woman was filling a pitcher from the river with one hand, and in the other she was holding a lighted piece of resinous wood. She had no idea that I was there; she placed her pitcher coolly on her head and, torch in hand, disappeared among the rushes. I followed her and found myself at the entrance to a cave.

The woman walked calmly forward and mounted a fairly steep slope; it was a sort of staircase cut out of the wall of a huge hall. In the torchlight I could see the floor of this hall, which was barely above the level of the river; but I could not make out its full extent. Without quite knowing what I was doing, I started climbing the slope behind the young woman with the torch, and followed her at a distance. Now and again her light disappeared behind some rocky projection, but I soon found her again.

I thought I could also make out the gloomy openings of great galleries leading into the principal room. It looked like a subterranean town with streets and crossroads. I stopped short, considering it dangerous to venture alone into that vast labyrinth.

Suddenly one of the galleries below me was lit up brightly, and I saw a great number of torches, which appeared to come out of the sides of the rocks to form a sort of great procession. At the same time a monotonous chanting arose, which recalled the singing of the Arabs as they recite their prayers.

Soon I could distinguish a vast multitude advancing slowly. At their head walked a black man, almost naked, his head covered with an enormous mass of shaggy hair. His long white beard contrasted with the brown colour of his chest, which was streaked with bluish tattoo marks. I immediately recognized the sorcerer of the previous evening, and soon after saw the little girl near him who had played the part of Eurydice, with her beautiful eyes, her silk pantaloons, and her embroidered kerchief on her head.

Women, children, and men of all ages followed them, all holding torches, all dressed in strange, brightly coloured costumes, with trailing skirts and high caps, some made of metal, which reflected the light from the torches on all sides.

The old sorcerer stopped exactly below me, and the whole procession with him. A profound silence fell. I was twenty feet above him, protected by some big stones, from behind which I hoped to see everything without being noticed. At the old man's feet I saw a large slab of stone, almost round, with an iron ring in the centre.

He pronounced a few words in a tongue unknown to me, which I feel sure was neither Arabic nor Kabylic. A rope and pulleys, hanging from heaven knows where, fell at his feet; it was fastened to the ring, and at a given signal twenty stalwart arms all pulled at once. The stone, which seemed to be very heavy, was raised and put on one side.

I then saw what looked like the opening of a well, the water of which was less than a yard from the top. Water, did I say? I do not know what the frightful liquid was; it was covered over with an iridescent film, broken in places, and showing a hideous black mud beneath.

Standing near the kerbstone round the well, the sorcerer rested his left hand on the little girl's head; and with his right he made some strange gestures, while uttering a kind of incantation in the midst of general silence.

From time to time he raised his voice as if he were calling someone. 'Djoumane! Djoumane!' he cried; but no one came. In the meantime he rolled his eyes and ground his teeth, making raucous cries which did not seem to come from any human breast. The old rascal's mumbo-jumbo irritated me and filled me with indignation; I felt tempted to hurl at his head one of the stones that I had ready to hand. When he had yelled the name of Djoumane for perhaps the thirtieth time, I saw the iridescent film over the water tremble, and at this sign the whole crowd drew back; the old man and the little girl alone remained by the side of the hole.

Suddenly a huge bubble of bluish mud rose from the well, and out of this mud came an enormous snake's head, of a pale grey colour, with phosphorescent eyes. . . .

Involuntarily I leapt backwards. I heard a little cry and the sound of a heavy body falling into the water. . . .

When I looked down again, perhaps a tenth of a second later, I saw the sorcerer standing alone by the well-side; the water was still bubbling, and in the middle of what remained of the iridescent scum there floated the kerchief which had covered the little girl's hair. . . .

Already the stone was being moved, and it fell into place over the aperture of the horrible gulf. Then all the torches were simultaneously extinguished, and I was left in the darkness in the midst of a silence so profound that I could distinctly hear my heart beating. . . .

As soon as I had recovered a little from this ghastly scene I decided to leave the cave, vowing that if I succeeded in rejoining my comrades, I would return to exterminate the abominable denizens of this place, men and snakes alike.

But the pressing question was how to find my way out. I had come, I believed, about a hundred yards into the cave, keeping the rock wall on my right.

I turned round, but I could see no light indicating the entrance to the cave; however, it did not extend in a straight line, and besides, I had climbed up all the time from the river bank. I groped along the rock with my left hand, and sounded the ground with the sword which I held in my right, advancing slowly and cautiously. For a quarter of an hour or twenty minutes—perhaps even half an hour I walked on without being able to find the entrance.

I was seized with anxiety. Had I, without noticing, entered some side gallery instead of returning the way I had come at first?

I was still going forward, feeling the rock all the time, when in place of the cold stone I felt a curtain, which yielded to my touch and let through a ray of light. Taking greater care than ever, I drew the curtain noiselessly aside and found myself in a little passage leading to a well-lighted room. The door was open, and I saw that this room was hung with tapestry embroidered with golden silk flowers. I could make out a Turkish carpet and part of a velvet-covered divan. On the carpet was a silver hookah and several perfume-burners. In short, it was an apartment sumptuously furnished in the Arabian style.

I approached with stealthy tread until I reached the door; a young woman was squatting on the divan, and near it was a little low table of inlaid wood, which held a large silver-gilt tray full of cups and bottles and bunches of flowers.

On entering this subterranean boudoir I felt quite intoxicated by some exquisite perfume.

Everything in this retreat breathed voluptuousness; on every side I saw the glitter of gold and sumptuous materials, varied colourings, and rare flowers. The young woman did not notice me at first; her head was bent and she was pensively fingering the amber beads of a long necklace. She was extremely beautiful. Her features were like those of the unfortunate child I had seen below, but more finely formed, more regular, and more voluptuous. Her hair, as black as a raven's wing and 'as long as a king's cloak', fell over her shoulders and the divan down to the carpet under her feet. A bodice of transparent silk with broad stripes hinted at splendid arms and breasts. A velvet tunic braided with gold fitted closely round her waist, and her short blue satin pantaloons revealed a marvellously tiny foot, from which hung a golden Turkish slipper which she swung up and down in a graceful, idle movement.

My boots creaked, and she raised her head and saw me.

Without showing the least embarrassment or surprise at seeing a stranger with a sword in his hand come into her room, she clapped her hands gleefully and beckoned me to come nearer. I greeted her by placing my hand first on my heart and then on my head to show her that I was acquainted with Mohammedan etiquette. She smiled at me, and with both hands she put aside her hair which covered the divan— this was to tell me to sit down beside her. I thought all the perfumes of Araby were coming from those beautiful locks.

I modestly sat down at the far end of the divan, inwardly vowing that I would soon go much closer. She took a cup from the tray, and holding it by the filigree saucer, she poured out some coffee. Then, after touching it lightly with her lips, she offered it to me.

'Ah, Roumi! Roumi . . . !' she said.

'Won't you have a drink, Lieutenant?'

At these words I opened my eyes wide. This young woman had enormous mustachios, and was the living image of Sergeant Wagner. . . . And it was indeed Wagner who stood in front of me offering me a cup of coffee, while I, pillowed on my horse's neck, stared at him in amazement.

'It looks as if we've had a nap all the same, Lieutenant. Here we are, at the ford, and the coffee's boiling.'